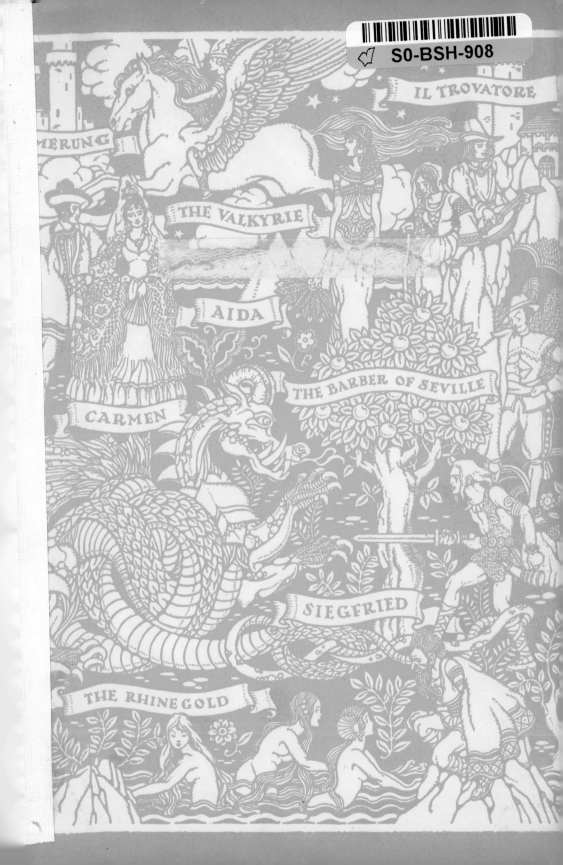

April 17, 1951

Wilbur F. Snyder

THE PRIZE SONG

THE·PRIZE·SONG
STORIES·OF·FAMOUS·OPERAS
by
HENRIETTE WEBER

FOREWORD BY DOROTHY LAWTON
MUSIC LIBRARIAN *of* THE NEW YORK PUBLIC LIBRARY

ILLUSTRATED BY
MARIE·A·LAWSON

OXFORD UNIVERSITY PRESS
LONDON · NEW YORK · TORONTO

PRINTED IN THE UNITED STATES OF AMERICA

CONTENTS

CONTENTS

FOREWORD

IN every epoch of the world's history, music, of all the arts, though among the first evolved, has been among the latest developed. Not until the seventeenth century could music stand alone, and as pure tone, independent of Poetry, Drama or the Dance, deliver its message in absolute forms. This of course could not be accomplished until the making of instruments arrived at such a degree of excellence that they could imitate, if not parallel, the human throat or the voices of Nature.

At the close of the Italian Renaissance, when, already, Literature, Architecture, Sculpture and Painting had revived "the glory that was Greece", an attempt was made to re-introduce Greek Drama. It was in a room in the Bardi Palace in Florence, the cradle of the Renaissance, that there was born in the year 1600, a new form of art which was destined to engage musically creative minds and the genius of dramatists, poets, painters, and all artisans of the theatre to this day. This new art was appropriately called *opera*, meaning *works*.

The discovery of the form of opera was more accidental than deliberate. In the open-air theatres of Greece it had been found that the voice carried better if the words were intoned—or sung—rather than spoken. Consequently, the poets and dramatists of the ancient Greeks always placed a musical notation over the syllables of their poetic writings. When Jacopo Peri, in the year 1600, brought out his drama *Eurydice* for the Bardi Society, he found that the music with which he accompanied it, in the approved Greek fashion, had grown so in the fifteen or more centuries of progress, that it *dominated* rather than *accompanied* the text. When the young elegantes who comprised the Bardi Society heard the work they immediately recognized a new form of art differing from, and out-distancing, all their expectations.

When, five years later in Venice, Monteverde produced his *Orfeo*, another version of the same classic subject, opera proved to be an ideal medium for the presentation of his new theory of composition, the monophonic harmony, in which one voice carrying the principal melody was supported by the others as accompaniment. This brought the soprano voice into great prominence and led to the employment of women in public performance where only boy sopranos and tenor falsetti had been used before. From that time opera became the favourite secular form of writing with the facile composers of the 17th and 18th centuries as well as the most popular form of musical entertainment with the ladies and gentlemen of the court. It was, and still is, the favourite form of art with Italians of every class. It is they who crowd the upper galleries of the opera-houses the world over and who stand in line for hours for the privilege of applauding an aria from the lips of a favourite diva.

But the making of opera did not confine itself to Italy. Jean Baptiste Lully, an Italian, took his work into France and became the principal musical influence at the court of Louis XIV. Here he shared the royal favour and honours with Moliere and even collaborated with this greatest of French dramatists on several occasions.

About this time the Singspiel or singing play began to appear in Germany. This was generally based on peasant themes and appealed to the populace more than the aristocratically designed French and Italian operas. In England the masques of the court of King James I were followed by the dramatic cantatas and ballet-mimes of Purcell, which led again to the ballad-operas of the 18th century, where the lyrics of a play were sung to the popular songs of the period and strung together with incidental music. Gay's *Beggars' Opera* was the best example of this type, where Gay, the writer of the libretto, is credited as the author of the opera while the name of Pepusch, the composer and arranger of its music, is scarcely known at all.

Near the close of the 18th century a disagreement with the management of the Opera Française caused a number of the caste to break away and form a separate company of their own. Their new locale together with their desire for independence led to a slight variation in the form of their performances, and their new compositions as well as their new company became known as Opera Comique. The difference lay mainly in the occasional interpolation of spoken lines to relieve the singing. Their plots were not always comic as the name implied, but frequently had a tragic ending. Some of the best examples of French operatic writing have been produced under these auspices. But the most ambitious and best known writers of the 17th, 18th and early 19th centuries have written opera in the Italian manner. Handel, Mozart, Beethoven, Gluck and Weber all wrote to Italian libretti and after the Italian pattern. The two last, however, began to show an independence of spirit and paved the way for the great revolutionary philosopher and epochmaker, the greatest operatic writer of all time, whose work was the glory of the 19th century—Richard Wagner.

Such in very brief is the history of the origins of opera. A knowledge of this form of art should, of necessity, be in the consciousness of all cultured people whether they are educated musically or not.

The United States of America were founded in a spirit of protest against existing governmental conditions in Europe and, generally speaking, have followed the rigid Hebrew standards of perfection rather than the more gracious Greek ideals of beauty. As a nation, therefore, we have followed the historic tradition in the progress of art. The first work to be printed in the North American continent was the Bay Psalm Book of the Massachusetts Colony which contained the metrical version of the Psalms with the tunes used in the services by the Pilgrim Fathers. This book was taken to England and Holland and used among the Puritans of those countries and thus was the first contribution to art in any form that came from the New World. Soon after this, Literature, Architecture, Painting and Drama made themselves felt, and, while fashioned from European patterns, showed certain unmistakable national characteristics. Music, however, until very lately, has been tied far too closely to the mother countries. But now, in the fourth century after its colonization and in the second century of its national existence, America has become music-conscious. The United States possesses the most famous orchestras of the world. It has an opera-house counted the most brilliant of modern times and has been the artistic Mecca of every prima donna for the past half-century. An appreciable wave of musical talent is breaking over the country. Every effort is being made throughout the country to train the rising generation in this art and to make a knowledge of music as much a part of general education as the three R's.

The publication of such a book as *The Prize Song, Stories of Famous Operas* at this juncture is most timely. This book, written by Henriette Weber who is Music Critic of the New York Evening Journal, is intended for children between the ages of eight and fifteen. Its patrons, however, need consider no such limitations. Any tyro in operatic literature may have his interest caught by the perusal of its pages. The volume's very format, its end-papers, its illustrations, all combine to evoke the mood of opera. There have been certain so-called "shirt-waist" operas whose characters wear more or less modern dress and behave in manner like unto ourselves, but these seem, somehow, strange and appear to have wandered into an environment not their own. Opera in its old tradition should carry us beyond the mundane, should waft us to the regions of fancy and of magic. Its actors should tread the stage in the grand manner; its characters should be kings and queens and princes, if not gods and goddesses. The operas discussed in this little book fulfill in great measure all these requirements. All the fifteen works described are contained in the standard operatic repertory. Six are Italian, two French, and seven of the greatest master of all—Richard Wagner.

There may be similar publications, but we are not aware of any book of opera for children which, having no pretension to analyze the musical content or explain the under-lying meaning of the libretto, gives so well the straightforward story of the work. Leading themes are introduced in musical text in their proper places in the narrative. Two-toned illustrations are designed to awake in the childish mind a picture of the ideal heroes and heroines. It is interesting to note here that these illustrations supplant the usual photographic representations of the singers who have interpreted the parts. These photographs, while they may have had a commemorative value in recalling the personalities of the great artists who have created the rôles, have probably helped to build up that star-system of appreciation that has been for so long a deplorable characteristic of the American musical public.

A most valuable appendix to this book contains half-minute histories of each opera for the attention of the parent or teacher. These tell of its world première, its first appearance in New York, some of the artists who created the leading rôles and other items of interest concerning its career.

A few years ago a committee was formed with the desire of arranging for the school children of New York and its environs opportunity to have presentations of Art in the best obtainable manner, given without compromise or concession to immature intelligence. The plan was to give each child a visit to a painting exhibition, to a symphony concert, a classic play and an opera matinee. The first of these artistic adventures —selected after much prayerful cogitation on the part of the committee— was a performance of *Die Meistersinger* at the Metropolitan Opera House. This opera was chosen as possessing the highest qualifications for youthful study. Its narrative is founded on historic fact, its plot is charming, amusing and of consummate literary value and its music has every element of greatness. As a member of that committee I feel particularly glad that this book should begin with this opera and bear its name.

Although these fifteen are perhaps the best-known of the standard operas, there are many more of equal merit that should not be neglected. The limits of one volume prevent the inclusion of more than this number, but we are left with the hope that this may soon be followed by Volume II or even be the first of a series devoted to the growing understanding of the Arts.

DOROTHY LAWTON.

New York, 1935.

PUBLISHER'S NOTE

The music excerpts which illustrate the two operas by Puccini, *Madame Butterfly* and *La Bohème*, are used with the kind permission of G. Ricordi and Company, Milan.

To J. G.
whose loyalty to my
"Opera Evenings"
has made this book possible

THE PRIZE SONG

or
THE MASTERSINGERS
❋ *by* RICHARD WAGNER ❋

The Prize Song

THE people living in the quaint old town of Nuremberg, the town of "art and song", were in a state of great excitement. Tomorrow would be St. John's Day. This great feast day was always celebrated with great festivities, but this year there was to be an event of special importance, a song festival, in which the Mastersingers would compete for a prize. The winner would not only achieve artistic glory but also win a bride! All the bachelor members of the guild were especially interested, as well they might be.

The "bride-to-be" was Eva, the popular daughter of Veit Pogner, a rich goldsmith and a leading citizen. The plan of suggesting his daughter as a prize had been devised by Pogner to give added interest to the song competition, and to silence those critics who declared that the good citizens who made up the ranks of the guild cared more for money and worldly success than for the ideals of art.

"I will show them," declared Pogner. "The victorious Mastersinger may have my greatest treasure—provided, of course, that Eva is willing to accept him!"

In consequence, the whole town was in a state of eager anticipation. Busy gossips discussed who the lucky man might be and whether Miss Eva would have him. When the announcement was made one of the older Masters was heard to grumble, "Would we were all bachelors!" And Hans Sachs, the elderly bachelor and "cobbler poet", who, in spite of his years, had a secret desire to win the lovely Eva for himself, replied, "Some might willingly give up their wives!"

In order to appreciate why a song competition was of such great public interest four hundred years ago, we must first know what a Mastersingers Guild actually was. Knowing this will also help us to understand what Richard Wagner had in mind when he composed this amusing opera, the only one of all his works written in a spirit of comedy and fun.

During the fourteenth and fifteenth centuries in Europe poetry and music began for the first time to be enjoyed by the so-called "common" people who started to organize art or music guilds everywhere. These guilds reached their greatest glory in the sixteenth century, and their influence is felt even to this day. Before the activities of the guilds, writing poetry and composing songs were arts for kings and nobles, and the songs of those earlier days were mostly sentimental ballads and love songs which gallant troubadours sang under the windows of fair ladies.

With the coming of the guilds, music-writing became wide-spread, and took on so many rules and forms that it became a serious matter to attempt to compose a song. In the sixteenth century Nuremberg became one of the noted centers for the guilds. It was at this time that it gave the world the great painter, Albrecht Dürer, and also the famous cobbler poet, Hans Sachs, who figures importantly in this opera.

Those who belonged to the singing guild were called "Mastersingers," (Meistersinger) and were admitted to membership only after they had learned the technical requirements of a true master-song. Many of the rules governing their music-writing were unnecessary and foolish and hampered the development of new creative talent. To make matters worse, some of the Masters who were teachers in the guild or judges at the competitions were narrow-minded and unprogressive in their regulations against new and original ideas.

The criticism which Richard Wagner was forced to meet in his own life is reflected in this attitude of the ancient guilds. Being the most revolutionary opera composer the world has known, he was so far ahead of his time that his career was a continuous battle for recognition of his "new" art. Petty-minded "professors" and critics who were too narrow to recognize his genius, wrote scathing criticisms of his work. They could only be sure of the old and established music and they could not understand anything else.

Wagner in his wide search for material for his operas found that these ancient music guilds with their many "don'ts" provided him with a chance to rebuke his own ignorant critics. He therefore composed this opera around the practices of a sixteenth century Mastersingers Guild, making the young knight, Sir Walther, give his own progressive ideas and win a victory for the newer music.

In the opera many of the Masters, with the exception of the far-seeing Hans Sachs and big-hearted Pogner, are represented as bigoted and ignorant. Of these narrow-minded men Beckmesser is the worst example, and he is Sir Walther's worst enemy.

The opera begins with an orchestral prelude which introduces the main themes including the stately Mastersingers March which is heard again in all its glory during the closing scene of the opera.

Mastersingers March

When the curtain rises on the first act we see the interior of St. Catherine's Church in Nuremberg. The congregation is singing a hymn and our attention is at once attracted to the pew where a pretty girl, Eva Pogner, is sitting. She is apparently less interested in the church service than in a handsome young knight who leans against a pillar at the far side of the church and stares fixedly in her direction.

The young man is Walther von Stolzing, a nobleman who has arrived in Nuremberg to transact business with Eva's father. While at her home the day before he had met Eva and they had fallen in love at first sight. Eva knows nothing of the business which has brought Sir Walther to Nuremberg but assumes that he has come to compete in the song festival in which she is so deeply interested. The knight, however, knows nothing of the contest, but, after seeing Eva, has remained in the town with the hope of meeting her again.

Here in the church the young people carry on a constant exchange of glances until the service is over, when Walther steps up and greets Eva. She is delighted and, wishing to be alone with him for a few minutes, she quickly invents an excuse to get rid of her maid, Magdalena, sending her back to their pew where, Eva says, she has left her handkerchief. Magdalena comes back entirely too soon to suit the lovers and her mistress sends her back for a shoe buckle she has "lost." She then makes poor Magdalena return a third time for the prayer book she says she has "forgotten."

Meanwhile Walther learns that Eva is not betrothed and is free to marry but that she is to be the bride of the winner at tomorrow's song festival. She now explains that the "trial song" meeting of the guild, open to candidates who wish to appear at the festival, is to take place within the hour in this very church. Walther resolves, without a moment's hesitation, to sing for the guild and tells Eva of his decision. She is overjoyed and secretly prays for his success. Then she regretfully leaves with Magdalena.

While Eva and Walther have been talking together a number of choir boys and apprentices have come in to arrange the nave of the church for the meeting of the Mastersingers Guild. A dark curtain has been drawn to shut off the altar, and benches for the Masters are placed in an imposing semi-circle. One of the most active workers is David, apprentice to Hans Sachs. He directs the younger boys at their tasks, chiding the laggards who are inclined to play jokes on each other rather than to attend to their duties.

In spite of his labors, David has found time to exchange a few words with Magdalena, to whom he is devoted, and both of them have noted with sympathetic interest the growing infatuation between Eva and Walther. When Eva and her maid take their departure Walther remains in the church somewhat absent-mindedly watching the preparations for the guild meeting, and musing upon the surprising situation in which he finds himself. He is proficient in the arts of poetry and music, but he has never aspired to be a mastersinger—certainly not in a tradesmen's guild! But his love for Eva and the knowledge that she will give her hand in marriage to the winning singer has changed everything for the young knight.

The fact that he knows nothing of the technical rules governing the guild does not alarm him. He is confident that he will win, regardless of anything that may stand in his way. Watching David, who appears to be directing things, Walther singles him out and questions him regarding the rules of the guild. David is somewhat embarrassed by the grandeur of the young nobleman and becomes so confused in his replies that many of them are comical. The more he tries to explain the rules of song-writing as practiced by the guild, the more he gets them mixed up with his shoe-making craft which he knows much better.

"But I don't want to be a shoemaker," Walther finally breaks in, impatiently, "I want to know the rules for writing a master-song!" So David continues, as best he can, to tell about line and phrase and rhythm and pitch and confesses that he has tried for years to master all these intricate rules, but has not yet been able to make the "master" grade.

"H-m-m-m," muses Walther. "All this is very interesting, but I have my own ideas about rules for rhythm and melody and musical expression. I am not going through the preliminaries. I intend to be a 'master' from the start!''

David shrugs his shoulders in astonishment at the sublime confidence of the stranger and turns his attention once more to what his assistants are doing. A small platform has been erected with curtains around it, and behind these curtains the official "marker" is to stand, listening to the trial songs that are presented and marking on a blackboard any mistakes or broken rules. When word goes around among the boys that the young knight is to offer a trial song without any preparation, they form a ring around him and sing him a song of good luck.

Song of the Apprentices

The boys scatter in confusion when Pogner and Beckmesser enter. Pogner is explaining to Beckmesser that Eva must be permitted to express her own wishes in the matter of accepting the prize winner, and that he has no intention of forcing his beloved daughter to make an unhappy marriage. This irritates Beckmesser, the crabbed, ugly, disagreeable and learned Master of the Rules. He fully expects to win in tomorrow's contest, but now he protests. "If you let the girl have her own way," he says, "what good will my art do me?"

"You will have to have 'art' enough to win her, that is all," says Pogner who does not particularly fancy Beckmesser for a son-in-law. Catching sight of Sir Walther, Pogner greets him delightedly. "I did not expect you to look for me here at the guild meeting, Sir Walther," he exclaims.

Walther blandly explains that his main reason in coming to Nuremberg was not the business he transacted with Pogner, but rather to apply for membership in the famous Mastersingers Guild. This pleases Pogner beyond measure, but greatly chagrins Beckmesser who makes disparaging remarks under his breath.

Soon other members of the guild arrive. Pogner formally presents

Walther as the newest candidate for "Master" honors, and announces that he is prepared to offer a "trial song" to prove his fitness for membership. The roll call follows and Master Kothner, the leader for the day, appoints Beckmesser—of all people!—to be the "marker." That gentleman, wearing a mean grin, disappears behind the curtains of the platform, but not without a few sarcastic remarks to the young knight.

Master Kothner asks Walther the regulation questions about his training, to all of which the knight replies at length. Then Kothner presents the rules for composing a "Master" song and illustrates the different points by singing them.

How Kothner Sings the Rules

must have its spec-ial mel-o-dy and
from the oth-er diff-'rent be—

Walther is secretly amused, not so much at his pompous manner, as at the long runs and trills with which he embellishes his vocal efforts. All of it seems very unlike what Walther believes to be true beauty in a song. At last the Masters settle themselves to listen and Beckmesser, poking his head out of the curtains, shouts crossly to Walther, "Now, begin!"

Repeating the words, "Now, begin!" as the opening phrase of his song, Walther presents an impassioned melody well suited to the poetic words of his improvised text.

Walther's Trial Song

Deep feeling and artistic expression mark his performance, but as he ends the first part Mr. "Marker" Beckmesser's loud scratchings on the blackboard can be heard. Though slightly disconcerted, the knight continues his song, ending the second verse with the words:

And life pours forth with splendor
A glorious song of love.

Beckmesser fairly tears the curtains apart and cries rudely, "Haven't you finished? Look at the blackboard! It's covered with chalk marks! You broke all the rules! Your song was terrible!"

Some of the Masters start to laugh at Beckmesser's comical fury but others, following his lead, make disparaging remarks about Walther's composition. The knight, astounded at their rude behavior, cries, "Are you going to be so ungracious as not to let me finish my song?"

Hans Sachs and Pogner seek to quiet the others and at last bring about a temporary truce so that Walther can resume his song. This time murmurs of disapproval can be heard almost immediately and, as these grow louder, Walther himself grows angry. Changing the character of his song, he turns the last few measures into a sarcastic "farewell" to the Masters and, amidst a hubbub of confusion, dashes away before Pogner or Hans Sachs can stop him.

The Masters all talk at once as Beckmesser gleefully strides from one to the other showing his board covered with chalk marks. Only Pogner and Sachs refuse to listen to him and Sachs makes an eloquent plea for Walther's song which he found "beautiful, although so new." But the Masters will have none of it because he has broken all their sacred rules. So, in spite of his two defenders, the knight is officially declared to be "outdone, outsung, and rejected by the guild!"

The next scene takes place a few hours later, when twilight is falling. The stage shows one of the picturesque streets in this town of high gabled houses. On one side is the imposing home of Veit Pogner. A flight of stone steps leads up to it and a linden tree shades the garden in front. Opposite is the humble dwelling and workshop of Hans Sachs, the cobbler poet and friend of all the town.

David, Hans Sachs's apprentice, is closing the shutters for the night while other lads are seen doing the same elsewhere. A group of them come laughing and chatting down the street at the same moment that Magdalena comes out of the Pogner house and calls to David in a low voice. He does not hear her so the boys begin to call his name, mimicking her voice. Not to be fooled, David tells them to keep quiet. Then, look-ing around, he sees Magdalena waiting for him and runs toward her. She holds up a basket of goodies she has prepared for him, but then draws it away, saying, "Tell me, first, how did the knight get along at the trial song meeting today?"

Somewhat crestfallen David has to admit Walther's complete failure with the guild. Magdalena exclaims her disappointment. "But what is that to you?" asks David. Magdalena only shakes her head and runs back to the house, taking the basket with her. She knows how disheart-ening this news will be to her young mistress.

The boys gather around David and torment him shouting, "Oh, we saw her take the basket away! Magdalena has gone back on you. Yah! Yah!" until David can stand it no longer. He strikes at them with both fists and is still pommeling several of his tormentors when Master Sachs comes down the street.

"Here, you young rascals," he says sternly, "home, every mother's son of you. David, I am surprised to see you fighting these younger lads."

"Oh, Master, please forgive me," David says ruefully. "They did torment me so!"

Soon after this Master Pogner and Eva come strolling toward their home and pause to seat themselves on a bench under the linden tree for the evening is mild. Eva, who seems restless, keeps glancing down the street as though expecting someone and is visibly relieved when Magda-lena appears at the door to announce that supper is almost ready. This gives Eva an excuse to hurry her father into the house. As he disappears she lingers without and Magdalena comes to tell her in excited whispers the news of Walther's rejection by the guild.

"Oh, now what can we do?" cries Eva.

"Perhaps Master Sachs can advise you," suggests Magdalena. Eva, thinking this is good advice, steals across the street to his door where she is heartily welcomed. The cobbler poet has known Eva since she was a little motherless child and now, in his sympathetic way, he draws from her a confession of her deep interest in the young knight and her dis-appointment at his failure to qualify for the song festival. Realizing her real feeling behind this "interest", the elderly bachelor stifles his own secret love for the young girl and resolves to do all he can to aid her.

At this moment Magdalena calls to Eva to say that her father is asking for her. As Eva reaches her own door, the faithful servant stops her with another piece of unwelcome news: Beckmesser intends to serenade Eva that very evening, perhaps to soften her heart toward him for the morrow!

"How provoking!" cries the distracted girl. "You will have to stand in my bedroom window and pretend you are me," declares Eva. "And be sure to get rid of him somehow!" Eva is hoping to have a quiet meeting with Sir Walther in the garden. As Magdalena turns to go inside Eva calls after her, "Tell father I am not feeling well and won't want any supper!" Eva has just caught a glimpse of Sir Walther coming toward her.

He can scarcely wait to tell her of his unhappy experience before the guild. Eva does her best to console him, declaring that she loves him all the more and that she cares only for him and not at all for the guild or the festival tomorrow! This leads Walther to urge that they elope at once. He explains that he has horses and servants waiting nearby, but that they must manage to get away without Master Pogner seeing them. Eva rushes into the house while Walther walks up and down impatiently. She soon reappears, somewhat poorly disguised in one of Magdalena's dresses, and they withdraw into the shadows of the garden to await their chance to get away.

In the quiet of the evening the excited voices of the lovers have carried across the narrow street and Master Sachs, working by his open window, has overheard their plan. Although he is wholly in sympathy with the young people, he believes that another and better way may be found and he determines, in his wise and kindly fashion, to interfere. He opens his front door, carries his work bench outside, and sets a large lamp at his elbow which throws its light across the street, thus balking the lovers in their plan to escape unseen in the darkness.

Sachs pretends to be quite unaware of the situation and begins to hammer away at shoes he is making for Master Beckmesser. Just then that worthy appears with his lute under Eva's window and in a quavering voice attempts a romantic serenade while Magdalena, in a gown belonging to her mistress, stands in the window to fool him. Sachs has little liking for the unfortunate serenader, all the less so since Beckmesser's viciously antagonistic treatment of Sir Walther earlier that day. Now, when Beckmesser begins to sing, if it can be called that, Sachs begins to hammer loudly at his work, at the same time singing a jolly cobbler's song. Beckmesser, ill-tempered at best, grows furious and stops his serenading to yell at the cobbler to cease his noise, but Sachs pays no attention to him. The louder Beckmesser shouts, the louder the cobbler sings.

It happens that the quiet citizens of Nuremberg are given to retiring early, even on summer nights, and now night-capped heads appear at first one window and then another demanding what all the noise is about. "Who is bawling? Stop that yowling!" they shout.

David wakes up in his room at the back of Master Sachs's house and looking out he sees Magdalena, apparently listening to the efforts of a serenader in the garden below. With one bound he is out of bed and in another moment over in Pogner's garden, pommeling his supposed rival black and blue until Beckmesser cries for mercy. Men and boys come running from every direction to join in the fun and soon there is a general riot. While most of the fighting is all in good fun, it creates so much noise and confusion that Walther whispers to Eva, "Now is our time," thinking they can dash through the crowd without being noticed.

As they run across the street Master Sachs stops them with a friendly but imperious gesture. "Do not be rash," he says to them. Before they realize what is happening, he pushes Sir Walther through the open door of his shop and takes Eva to the steps of her father's house where he sees to it that she disappears within. Coming back to his own door he quickly calms Sir Walther, who is at first ready to resent this interference, and advises the young man to wait for another day, saying, "It may bring a better plan."

Meanwhile the good wives of the town have discovered that they can quickly stop the rioting by pouring water on the heads of their belligerent husbands. Their strategy works like a charm, the street is soon emptied, and once more a peaceful quiet settles upon the town.

The sleepy night watchman comes down the street, swinging his lantern. He stops and stares about him as though surprised. Rubbing his eyes he mutters, "Strange! I thought I heard shouts and sounds of rioting . . . . but all is quiet." He shakes his head and slowly plods down the street, blowing on his big ox horn at intervals and chanting his watchman's song:

> Hark ye, good people! Listen to the bell.
> Eleven is the hour and all is well!
> God keep ye safe from spectre and from sprite
> And let no power of ill your souls affright!
> Praise the Lord of Heaven.

When the curtain rises on the next act it is the morning of the festival day. The sun is shining brightly and there is no hint of the turmoil of the night before. In his study the learned Master Sachs sits with a great book on his knee. He is so engrossed that he scarcely notices David who comes in and tip-toes about so that he may not disturb the Master.

After a time Sir Walther appears in the doorway and his host greets him with great cordiality. The young knight admits that he has had a good night's sleep, in spite of the upsetting events of the previous day, and what is more, he has had a wonderful dream—a beautiful song has come to him!

"Inspiration does come that way at times," encourages the cobbler poet. "Sing your song to me while I jot down the words so they will not be lost."

Sir Walther sings his inspired song, putting all his soul into the music. Hans Sachs listens, enraptured. "It is a master-song!" he cries. "You must sing it at the festival today! I will arrange it. And possibly you will also win a bride!" The young man can hardly believe his good fortune and hurriedly withdraws to practice the song which may change his whole life. Master Sachs goes with him.

No sooner have they left than Beckmesser appears on the scene. He is in a sad state after last night's affray for he is covered with bruises and suffers from a lame back and a black eye. Altogether he presents a sorry spectacle. The music comically reflects every awkward movement and even relates in tones Beckmesser's emotions as he recalls the embarrassing events of the night before. What can he do now? How can he sing at the festival? The song he has prepared has gone right out of his head!

Limping about, Beckmesser discovers the poem of Walther's song in Sachs's handwriting. "Ah! A trial song by Master Sachs which he did not use!" He looks about stealthily, and seeing he is unobserved, puts it in his pocket. At this moment Hans Sachs comes in. His kindly expression changes to one of sternness as his eyes light upon Beckmesser, and a further quick glance tells him that the precious slip of paper containing Walther's poem has disappeared. He suspects his visitor and tells him so. Beckmesser admits his guilt and, taking the paper from his pocket, says, "Oh, Master, let me compose to this. Then I will surely have a winning song!"

Master Sachs ponders a moment, and then says, "Very well, take the words and do with them what you can. But remember! It is *not* my poem." Beckmesser does not believe him, but on Hans Sachs's promise not to give him away, he takes his leave.

Eva comes in, begging kind Master Sachs to look at one of her dainty new shoes which hurts her. Master Sachs is a little amused at this, but pretends to take her seriously as he examines the tiny shoe. He is quite aware that Eva has come in the hope of seeing Sir Walther. When the young knight appears, ready for the festival, he stands spellbound at the sight of Eva—more beautiful than he has ever seen her! At the request of his host he sings his "dream" song once again, and Eva is moved to tears by its beauty. The Master's eyes, too, are moist as he departs with the lovers.

The last scene of the opera shows a broad expanse of flowery meadow with the town of Nuremberg in the distance. The Pegnitz, winding its way across the plain, is alive with gayly decorated boats which pull up in a constant stream and unload their passengers—men, women, and children. As members of the various guilds arrive with their families, they gather in picturesque groups under their respective guild banners— the bakers, the tailors, the shoemakers, and many others—each group singing their guild song.

A raised platform, decorated with flags, awaits the arrival of the Mastersingers, and before it is a smaller platform for the competing singers. The scene is a gala one, full of color and movement. At last, amid shouts of welcome, the Mastersingers arrive to the music of their own imposing march. The great gathering is finally complete when Master Pogner appears, escorting his daughter Eva, who is followed by her train of festival attendants, the prettiest girls of the town having been chosen for this honor.

Under the leadership of Hans Sachs the Mastersingers intone a chorus in which all the people join except Beckmesser, who can be seen off to one side, nervously trying to memorize the words of the stolen poem. Master Sachs then addresses the assembled multitude and reminds them of the purpose of the festival. After this Beckmesser, as a candidate for prize song honors, is announced.

His aching limbs totter under him when he steps in the singer's place and he cuts a ridiculous figure as he twists with nervousness. At last, after an awkward bow, he is ready to begin. He clears his throat, croaks the first few notes, and then his memory fails him. He remembers how the poem sounds, but as he gives it he substitutes words which sound similar but have a different meaning and make no sense. Added to this, his melody, so hastily "composed" that morning, is unmusical and commonplace.

The people look at each other and smile, and there are even titters here and there. Beckmesser wipes his brow which is damp with perspiration and fairly gasps for breath. At last, when his voice cracks on a high note, he gives up and storms off the platform, hurling accusations at Hans Sachs. "You did it! This is your song! You wrote it just to disgrace me, a Master!" and he runs away out of sight.

The people are stung into silence by this startling accusation. Then they all begin to murmur, "It cannot be true. . . . Hans Sachs would never write such drivel. . . . There is some mistake. . . ." Then Master Sachs himself rises and begins to speak in a gentle voice.

"My friends," he says, "this is not my song although I would be proud to be its author. If the words were sung correctly, you would soon know it for a masterpiece! I will now introduce one who can prove this. Here is the creator of the song." He motions to Sir Walther who comes forward, dignified and self-possessed. Then Master Sachs says, "Good People, I present my witness and beg you to listen to his song and judge for yourselves."

Walther steps to the platform and with only a moment's pause and a fleeting glance in the direction of Eva, he begins.

The Prize Song

The vast throng listens with growing emotion which turns into surprised delight, and at the end they cheer wildly for his song has touched all hearts. With unanimous approval they applaud Sir Walther as the victor, and Eva places the wreath of laurel on his head. Deeply moved, he and Eva solemnly join hands, and then, as if by common impulse, turn toward their good friend, Hans Sachs, to receive his blessing.

MADAME BUTTERFLY

or

THE STORY of CIO-CIO-SAN
by GIACOMO PUCCINI

Madame Butterfly

CHERRY-BLOSSOM land is the setting for the romantic story of little Cio-Cio-San, whom her friends call "Butterfly." She is small and pretty and dainty, but, in spite of her youth and delicate charm, she proves so strong and brave and determined that it is evident she is a "butterfly" only in name and appearance.

Cio-Cio-San, Butterfly, lived in the quaint and picturesque town of Nagasaki which lay on the hills of Kyusha Island above the sparkling blue waters of Nagasaki Harbor and looked for all the world as though a shower of Japanese fans had fluttered to rest against the hilly slopes. This harbor was important in naval strategy and it was not unusual to see great ships from foreign countries ride its sheltered waters.

At the time of this story, a battleship of the United States Navy is lying in the harbor. The ship, the *Abraham Lincoln,* has been stationed there for some time and her stay is to be considerably prolonged. This greatly pleases Lieutenant Pinkerton, one of the naval officers. Young and heedless—and selfish too, he has found his first visit to Japan both novel and amusing. He has taken whatever entertainment has come his way, but has not made any attempt to understand the Japanese character. He feels that the polite manners and the flowery compliments of the Orient can be brushed aside when one is bored.

For all his thoughtless gayety he has come to find life at Nagasaki strangely exciting since the day he first saw Cio-Cio-San dancing in the teahouse where she earned her living. When he showed his interest in Butterfly, a watchful "marriage broker" named Goro had offered to "arrange matters." It was the custom in Japan for the marriage of a geisha (a public dancer) to be arranged through payment of a sum of money.

Lieut. Pinkerton had accepted the offer carelessly. Such a marriage seems to him a light affair which will probably end with the season of cherry blossoms. But from the very first it has been a serious matter to Butterfly for she has fallen deeply in love with the young naval officer and has accepted him with unquestioned faith and confidence.

Since the story is laid in Japan, the composer has cleverly introduced an oriental flavor in the music of this opera. Harmonies, rhythmic effects, and tone colors peculiar to the Orient accentuate the picturesque background against which the story unfolds.

Orchestral Introduction

When the curtain rises on the first act, the beautiful scene shows a high hill on which stands a quaint little Japanese house surrounded by a flowery terrace. Below, in the background, the harbor and town of Nagasaki can be seen in the distance.

Lieut. Pinkerton, in the uniform of the United States Navy, is looking over his little house which he has bought from Goro, the marriage broker. Here Pinkerton intends to bring Cio-Cio-San as his "bride", after he marries her in native fashion: "Tied for nine hundred and ninety-nine years, but free to annul the marriage at any time!" The wedding is to take place this very day. The house, like the bride, has been bought from Goro on the same indefinite plan. It belongs to Pinkerton for the impressive period of nearly a thousand years—with the privilege of cancelling the arrangement any month!

The house seems to its prospective owner as elastic as the convenient business contract. Goro, exhibiting all its advantages, slides out a wall here, another one there, and pushes a third one back to show how rooms can appear and disappear as though by magic to suit one's needs and fancy. Then he claps his hands and three servants appear.

"These," he says, "will wait upon you and your wife," and he rubs his hands with satisfaction. The servants, two men and a woman, promptly fall to their knees before Pinkerton, their new master.

"What am I to call them?" Pinkerton asks.

"Gentle-Breeze-of-the-Morning, Ray-of-the-Golden-Sun, Sweet-Scented-Pine-Tree," Goro tells him.

"What foolish names," laughs Pinkerton unfeelingly. "I'll just call them 'Scarecrows'."

Fortunately his rudeness is not understood and Suzuki (Gentle Breeze), interpreting his smile as one of friendliness, says in poetic Japanese fashion, "Your Honor deigns to smile? Your smile is as fair as flowers. A smile conquers all and defies trouble. . . ."

Pinkerton, not understanding her, is bored by what he considers "chatter". Goro, seeing this, claps his hands and the three servants quickly reenter the house. A moment later the American Consul, Sharpless, a friend of Pinkerton's, arrives somewhat out of breath from the climb.

"Hello, Sharpless," Pinkerton greets him while Goro bows. Then, while the Consul is getting his breath and fanning himself with his hat, Pinkerton orders Goro to bring refreshments. Sharpless looks about admiringly as Pinkerton points out the magnificent view and laughingly explains the trickery of the little house and the convenient terms on which he has bought it.

The two men servants, preceded by Goro, bring comfortable wicker chairs and a small table on which they place bottles and glasses. Pinkerton offers Sharpless a drink and then tells him how pleasant it is to have "a fair maid in every port".

"That is all well enough," agrees the Consul, "but it is dangerous!"

Nothing can dampen the young officer's jovial mood and he continues to boast of this Japanese marriage which, on paper, is to last many years but can actually be annulled at any time. Finally, carried away by his exuberant spirits, he rises to the toast, "America forever!" in which Sharpless joins him.

The Toast

"Is the bride pretty?" Sharpless asks.

Goro, who has been listening, now approaches and describes Cio-Cio-San. "She is fair as a garland of flowers," he says, "and was bought for almost nothing—only a hundred yen." Sensing possible business, he offers to find a "bride" for the Consul, but the latter, although he smiles, shakes his head impatiently.

Left alone, the two Americans discuss the situation. Sharpless disapproves strongly of what his friend is about to do and tells him so. Pinkerton, irritated, refuses to listen. Then Sharpless reveals that Cio-Cio-San had visited the American Consulate the day before. The Consul himself had not seen her, but he explains, "I heard her speak, and her voice touched my very soul. Surely only love that is pure and true speaks like that."

Pinkerton laughs at his friend, offers him another drink, and as they raise their glasses he says, "Here's to our friends at home . . . and here's to the day when I shall have a *real* wedding and a *real* American wife!" Sharpless shakes his head over this heartlessness but there is nothing he can do.

The chatter of girlish voices is heard as Butterfly, surrounded by a group of her young friends, reaches the top of the hill. They make a colorful picture with their gay costumes and brilliant parasols.

"How young and care-free they look," remarks Sharpless a bit sadly.

Butterfly, pausing a moment to look at the wide view, says, "I am the happiest girl in all Japan!" Then seeing the men, she quickly closes her parasol and turns to her companions with the command, "B. F. Pinkerton. Down!" They all drop to their knees, and as soon as they rise, admiringly surround Pinkerton, fanning themselves vigorously. Pinkerton smiles and says something about its being a tiring climb up the hill.

"Not as trying to a bride as are the weary hours of waiting," Butterfly answers.

"What a pretty compliment!" Pinkerton says, but there is a note of sarcasm in his voice.

"I know better ones than that," Butterfly says shyly. "If you care to hear . . . ."

"Thank you, no!" Pinkerton interrupts her.

Sharpless, much interested, now engages Butterfly in conversation. " 'Miss Butterfly', how pretty! Your name was well chosen. Are you from Nagasaki?"

"Sir, I am," Butterfly replies. "My people were once wealthy." And then with innocent pride she turns to her friends. "Say so!" she commands them. In her pretty way she tells more about her family circumstances and says that she, like these friends, has had to earn her living as a geisha. Sharpless greatly enjoys her prattle and Pinkerton is amused and delighted. The Consul asks her if she has any sisters.

"No," Butterfly explains, "I have only my mother."

"A most splendid lady," Goro interposes.

"But dreadfully poor," Butterfly adds ingenuously.

"And where is your father?" Sharpless asks gently.

There is a surprised pause. "Dead," Butterfly tells him. Then, to break the embarrassing silence, she adds, "But I have other relatives. There is my uncle, the Bonze (a Buddhist priest)."

"A miracle of wisdom!" her friends exclaim.

"A fountain of eloquence," Goro puts in.

Pinkerton laughs. "Thank you, thank you, kind fate!"

"And I have another uncle," Butterfly goes on to say, "but he is . . . ." She hesitates and her friends say quickly, "He's a good-for-nothing!" Butterfly tries to silence them and says kindly, "Oh, just a little wanting," and taps her forehead.

But her friends have more to tell. "An everlasting tippler!" they exclaim.

"One thinker and one drinker—they make a pretty pair," Pinkerton observes.

To change the subject Sharpless asks Butterfly how old she is. She fences with him coyly and makes him pretend to guess, finally admitting to fifteen years. "I am old, am I not?" she asks.

"The age for playthings," says Sharpless, a note of pity in his voice. "And for sweetmeats," Pinkerton adds.

He now tells Goro to call the "Scarecrows" and have them arrange the small tables on which refreshments are to be served when the other guests arrive. These are seen coming up the hill and Goro advances to meet them, announcing them with importance. "The august High Commissioner, the Official Registrar, the relations!"

Pinkerton leads Sharpless off to one side to watch the grotesque procession as Butterfly meets them with great ceremony. "What a farce it all is," he remarks. "I am sure my future mother-in-law is the lady behind the huge fan of peacock feathers. And that shabby looking ninny, jumping up and down like a frog, must be the tippling uncle."

"In spite of them, you are mighty lucky," Sharpless tells him. "I hope this pseudo marriage will not get you into any trouble."

The relatives, full of curiosity but a little embarrassed, crowd together and ask Butterfly, "Which one is he?" She proudly points out Pinkerton, but one cousin says, "I don't find him handsome."

"A handsomer man you never saw, even in your dreams!" cries Butterfly loyally.

"I think he is attractive," her mother says, but the others have all kinds of comments to make. "She will probably look down on us, now" says one. "She isn't as pretty as she used to be," says another. "They will probably be divorced," says a third, but Goro tries to silence them. "Where are your manners?" he asks.

Butterfly solemnly introduces them to Pinkerton with the command: "Listen to me, all of you—one . . . two . . . three . . . down!" They all bow and then surround Pinkerton, chattering the usual flattering compliments. With a slight show of impatience, he invites them to partake of the refreshments which they do, somewhat greedily.

Pinkerton and Butterfly draw to one side, and she slowly takes from the big sleeves of her silk kimono a few precious possessions—ribbons, a mirror, a fan. Pinkerton watches with amusement. Then, as she draws out a long narrow sheath, he asks, "What is that?" "Something I hold sacred," Butterfly answers gravely. "And am I not to see it?" he urges. "Not here in public, if you please," she begs.

Goro whispers to Pinkerton, "It is the dagger sent by the Mikado to her father with a message . . . .". He imitates the action of hari-kari (cutting the throat), a mandate which loyal Japanese obey to "save face", as they call it, when their honor is in question.

"And her father?" Pinkerton asks in a low voice.

"Was obedient," Goro replies.

The Imperial Commissioner signifies that all is ready and Goro claps his hands calling for silence. All the guests gather in a circle, with Pinkerton and Butterfly in the center, and the brief Japanese marriage ritual is read by the Imperial Commissioner, after which the bride and bridegroom sign the "contract". Cio-Cio-San's friends then crowd around her, addressing her as "Madame Butterfly" but she corrects them. "Madame B. F. Pinkerton, now!" she says.

Sharpless and the Imperial Commissioner leave, after offering their congratulations. Soon after, shouts are heard from someone coming up the hill and the Bonze, Butterfly's uncle, appears. He has just heard that she has renounced the Buddhist faith of her forefathers. Since this means that she will be ostracised by her own people, he hurls dire prophecies of evil on Butterfly's bowed head. All the relatives join with him. Her mother alone tries to shield her but is roughly pushed aside. Pinkerton, out of patience with the entire company, tells them to go. Led by the Bonze, they storm down the hill.

38

Butterfly now realizes that she has only her husband to cling to. She bursts into tears and Pinkerton comforts her until she forgets her troubles in her present happiness and, under the starlit sky, they sing together of their love.

Duet

Three years have passed. As the curtain rises, the scene shows the inside of Butterfly's home where, for nearly three years, she has lived alone. Suzuki is still with her and has proved a faithful servant. Indeed, she has grown to love her gentle mistress and it is with deep sorrow that Suzuki begins to fear that the American husband will never return. She is seen on her knees before the shrine of Buddha, praying to her gods that Butterfly may "weep no more".

Suzuki's Prayer

Butterfly stands near, looking through an opening in the shosi, the screened wall, where she has a view of the harbor. She turns to her devoted servant and says, "Lazy and idle are the gods in Japan. The God my husband prays to will give an answer quickly, . . . only I am afraid he does not know we live here," she adds, naively.

As Suzuki rises Butterfly speaks of more practical matters. "Suzuki," she asks, "how soon will we be starving?"

The servant goes to a cabinet and takes out a few coins. "This is all we have," she says.

"But he will come!" Butterfly declares.

"I hope so," replies Suzuki sadly.

Butterfly does what she can to calm the servant's fears and, perhaps,

39

her own. She reminds Suzuki of what Pinkerton said when he left—that he would return "when the robins nest again". Finding the servant still unconvinced, Butterfly says, "I will tell you just how it will be."

In the song which follows Butterfly tells what she imagines will happen "one fine day" when a ship will glide over the water of the harbor—his ship! Then he will come, calling to her as he used to do . . . . at first she will hide, to tease him a little, and to give herself time so that she will not die of joy at this meeting.

One Fine Day

Suzuki goes out and Butterfly looks after her sadly, but she is not alone for long. To her surprise the American Consul comes to call upon her. This is the first time Sharpless has seen Butterfly since her wedding day, three years ago. Now he comes on a sad errand. He is accompanied by Goro, the marriage broker, who remains outside the house, but can be seen lingering within ear-shot. Goro, who has kept in touch with Butterfly's affairs, knows that Pinkerton left a few weeks after their marriage and has never written to his Japanese wife. It is generally understood by everyone except Butterfly that he has deliberately deserted her. Since this constitutes legal divorce in Japan, Goro has attempted on various occasions to interest Butterfly in other suitors, but always to her intense disgust and anger. He knows that she is desperately poor and that her relatives have cast her off because she has given up the faith of her people.

Goro has discussed the situation with the Consul who had heartily disapproved of the marriage in the first place. He is now greatly distressed since it is he who has been commissioned to tell Butterfly that Pinkerton is returning to Nagasaki but does not wish to see her because he has been married in America to a "real" wife!

Butterfly is delighted to see the Consul. She is solicitous for his comfort, has Suzuki bring in the smoking things, and then serves tea. Sharpless tries several times to lead up to his disagreeable message, but each time Butterfly innocently interrupts him with some hospitable attention. Finally he manages to tell her that he has had a letter from Pinkerton.

"How is his honorable health?" Butterfly asks, and being told that he is quite well she jumps up, crying, "Then I am the happiest woman in Japan!" Then she says to the Consul, "Please answer this question: When do robins nest in America?"

Sharpless is puzzled. "Why do you ask that?" he says.

Butterfly tells him that Pinkerton had told her that he would return when the robins nest. "But that has happened three times in Japan, since he went away," she explains. "Perhaps in America they do not nest so often," she says wistfully.

Sharpless swallows hard at this further proof of her faith in Pinkerton and Goro, who has been listening from the terrace, laughs. Although Butterfly is disturbed by this laughter, she presses Sharpless for an answer to her important question and he says lamely that he knows nothing about birds.

Once again he tries to get to the reading of the letter, but again she interrupts him, this time to tell him about that "detestable Goro" who has dared to come to her with offers of marriage from various suitors. "Now he offers me riches if I will marry a prince," she cries indignantly.

Goro breaks into the conversation to justify himself. "It is the wealthy Prince Yamadori," he explains to Sharpless. Then, in a low voice, he continues, "She is desperately poor and her relatives have cast her off."

Butterfly now sees the Prince waiting on the terrace with two servants carrying his gift of flowers. "There he is," she says to Sharpless. "I will let you judge of him."

Prince Yamadori enters, summoned by Goro, and bows ceremoniously to Butterfly. But he has scarcely seated himself when she asks with sarcasm whether he still intends to kill himself if she withholds her kisses. No matter what the embarrassed suitor replies to this and other questions, she has a sharp answer for him until he finds himself silenced.

Goro tells Sharpless that "she still considers herself married to Pinkerton."

"I do not *think* so. I *know* I am!" declares Butterfly who has overheard him.

"The law says desertion gives the wife the right of divorce," explains Goro.

Butterfly shakes her head. "Perhaps in Japan, but not in *my* country —the United States!" she says.

All three men are distressed over her self-delusion. While she occupies herself with the tea things Goro whispers to the others, "Mr. Pinkerton's ship is already signaled."

"Then there is no hope for me," Yamadori says sadly.

"Lieut. Pinkerton does not wish to see her," Sharpless tells them. "I have a letter here, from him—but you see!" He shrugs his shoulders, helplessly. When the others leave, Butterfly at once settles down to hear Sharpless read the letter, which she cannot read herself since it is written in English.

He begins, but with every word there is a joyous interruption from Butterfly so that he does not get far enough for her to learn the truth. All she gathers is that Pinkerton has written . . . . he is well . . . . he has thought of her . . . . she is not forgotten! Sharpless gives up. "The devil take Pinkerton!" he mutters to himself as he pockets the letter, but he makes one more effort to tell her the truth. Taking both of her hands in his he asks gravely, "What would you do, Madame Butterfly, if Pinkerton should never return?"

Butterfly looks at him for a moment as though she had had a death blow, then she says slowly, "I would go back to sing and dance for the people, or better, I would die."

Sharpless, distressed, paces up and down. Finally he says, "I hate to tear you from your illusions, but let me urge you to accept Yamadori."

"This, from you?" cries Butterfly. She claps her hands and tells Suzuki to show the Consul to the door. When he turns to go she regrets her action. "Forgive me," she cries, "but how can you say such things? Do you think I am forgotten?" Running from the room, she soon comes back with a fair-haired baby boy on her shoulder.

"The child is the very image of him," says Sharpless, deeply moved. "Does Pinkerton know?"

"No," Butterfly tells him. "He was born when his father was far off in his own country. But you will write and tell him?" she pleads. She places the child on a cushion on the floor and the sight of her playing with the boy is almost more than Sharpless can bear. "What is his name?" he asks.

"Today his name is 'Trouble', but when his father returns his name will be 'Joy' ", she explains.

"His father shall be told, that I promise you," Sharpless assures her and leaves.

He is scarcely gone when a cannon shot is heard, and Suzuki comes running in crying, "The harbor cannon. Look! It is a ship!" Butterfly runs out on the terrace with her.

"It is white . . . . white . . . . the American stars and stripes. It is putting into port!" Butterfly is almost breathless with excitement. She seizes a telescope from a table and dashes out on the terrace again. "Steady my hand so I can read the name—yes! . . . . yes! . . . . the *Abraham Lincoln!*"

Hysterical with happiness Butterfly cries, "We must get everything ready! How soon can he be here, do you think, Suzuki? In an hour? . . . . no . . . . perhaps two hours . . . .?"

She orders the servant to gather flowers with which to fill the room, and together they bring in great armfuls, singing joyously.

Flower Duet

Butterfly puts on her wedding dress, and places a red flower in her hair, while Suzuki helps her and dresses the baby in his best. The shosi is lowered so that they may look through it without being observed, and Butterfly makes three openings in it—one for herself, one lower down for Suzuki who crouches there, and the lowest for the baby.

The orchestra plays the following effective music to denote the passing of time:

Waiting

When the curtain rises again it is dawn, with the scene unchanged. Butterfly, who has watched through the long night, stands in the same spot. Suzuki and the child have fallen asleep. Suzuki wakes with a start and touches her mistress on the shoulder. "It is daylight!" she says.

"He will come! I know he will come!" Butterfly tries to sound confident. The servant begs her to lie down and rest and Butterfly reluctantly complies, singing softly to the sleeping child as she carries him up the stairs.

Someone knocks gently on the door and Suzuki, answering, is speechless with amazement at seeing Lieut. Pinkerton with the Consul. They motion to her not to make any sound. "Is she asleep?" whispers Pinkerton. "Do not disturb her."

"She was so weary. She stood all through the night waiting for you," Suzuki tells him.

"How could she know?" asks Pinkerton.

"Know?" Suzuki is surprised at his question. "No ship has crossed the harbor in the last three years that Madame Butterfly has not eagerly examined."

"Didn't I tell you?" says Sharpless. Then, as the servant turns to call Butterfly, they detain her. "Do not tell her yet," they both exclaim. Suzuki's attention is attracted to the garden by a slight sound, and she sees a strange lady standing there.

"Who is that?" she asks, alarm and suspicion in her voice.

"Better tell her everything," warns Sharpless, but Pinkerton, confused, stammers, "She . . . er . . . . came with me."

"She is his wife," Sharpless explains.

Suzuki falls to her knees, her face to the ground. Sharpless gently raises her and explains that they have come early in order to see her alone. The future of the child is important. This gracious lady would be a mother to it. Can Suzuki persuade Madame Butterfly to give up her child?

Overcome by a realization of his cruelty, Pinkerton leaves, once more putting on his friend the burden of telling the truth to Butterfly. Just then she is heard coming down the stairs. Suzuki tries to stop her but is brushed aside as Butterfly cries, "He is here, I know!" Then she stops. "But where?" she cries.

She sees first the Consul looking at her sadly . . . . then the strange lady . . . . Somehow she knows the truth before a word is spoken. Kate Pinkerton speaks gently of the father's hope that he may have his child, and Butterfly listens in silence. After a moment she finds her voice

and with quiet dignity asks the Consul and Pinkerton's wife to go, saying, "tell him to come for his son in half an hour."

Left alone, she goes to the shrine of Buddha in the corner of the room, bows before it, and then stands for a long time without moving or speaking. Her new God seems to have forsaken her and she returns to the faith of her ancestors. Slowly she takes from the shrine a long white veil which she hangs over the top of a screen at the back of the room. Then, drawing her father's dagger from its sheath, she reads the words on the blade:

> *To die with honor*
> *When one can no longer*
> *Live with honor.*

Just then Suzuki pushes the laughing child through the door, thinking he will bring the mother comfort. As he toddles toward her she catches up the baby and kisses him almost to suffocation. Then she places him on a cushion on the floor, puts a small American flag in his hand and a doll in his arms and tells him to play as she blindfolds him.

This done, she steps behind the screen. A moment later the dagger is heard to fall and the white veil is drawn down behind the screen. Butterfly, with the veil about her throat, staggers into the room and falls, dying, just as Pinkerton and Sharpless burst through the door.

CARMEN
or
A SPANISH GYPSY
by GEORGES BIZET

Carmen

WHEN the curtain rises on the first act of *Carmen* we see a square in the city of Seville. Three streets run into the square and they are lined with buildings that are characteristic of this fascinating Spanish city. Toward the front, at one side of the stage, is a guardhouse, and directly opposite is the entrance to a tobacco factory. Further back a flight of steps leads to a bridge.

A group of soldiers is lolling in the sun, smoking, chatting among themselves, and lazily watching the people who come and go across the square. The soldiers are waiting for the relief guard and the square gradually fills with people who want to watch the military ceremony of "guard mount."

Mingling with the crowd is Micaela, a fair-haired girl who gazes shyly and anxiously about her and finally looks toward the soldiers.

"That's a pretty girl over there," observes Morales, the corporal. "She seems to be looking for someone."

"She acts as though she would like to speak to us but is afraid," remarks one of the soldiers. "She needs encouragement."

Morales, following the suggestion, rises and walks toward Micaela. "Are you looking for someone, pretty one?" he asks.

"I am looking for a corporal," she replies.

"Indeed!" retorts Morales, twisting his mustache. "Won't I do?"

"Oh no! You are not the one," Micaela explains hastily. "His name is Don José. Do you happen to know him?"

"Why, yes! We all know him," Morales says smilingly. "He is the corporal of the other company of guards that will arrive shortly to relieve us."

49

"Then I think I must go now," says Micaela quietly, turning away.

"Why not wait here?" Morales suggests. Several of the soldiers who are standing near add their pleas to his and glance admiringly at the pretty girl. But Micaela shyly insists that she must go and leaves, saying that she will return after guard mount.

A bugle call, followed by the sound of a brisk military march, announces the arrival of the fife and drum corps of the relief guard. A crowd of street urchins cheer and throw their caps in the air as they follow along in time with the stirring music. Behind them the soldiers of the guard come marching over the bridge.

Military March

The soldiers in front of the guardhouse rise to attention at the command of their officer, file to the rack which holds their lances gayly decorated with small yellow and red flags and await the new guard. The brief ceremony of changing guards takes place with military precision and the retiring company marches off gayly followed by their admiring chorus of small boys. After the new guard breaks ranks the two officers in charge have a friendly chat. They are Zuniga, the captain, and Don José, the corporal.

At the sound of a bell which rings the noon hour, a crowd of girls come out of the tobacco factory to the delight of the young men who have been waiting for them in the square. They meet and talk together with much laughter, cigarette smoking, and singing.

Don José, the corporal, young and good-looking in his red and yellow uniform, takes off his helmet, seats himself on a chair in front of the guardhouse and busies himself with a small chain he is mending. He pays little attention to what is going on about him. Suddenly the men cry "There she is!" and Carmen, a Spanish gypsy, comes running across the bridge. She has a flower in her mouth and she pauses to look about her coquettishly, conscious, perhaps, that she is the prettiest of all the factory girls. Don Jose surveys her indifferently and continues his work.

Carmen elbows her way along, nudging first one young man, then another. As they crowd around her she smiles at all of them and shows her white teeth. She twirls the flower in her hand and begins to sing in a provoking manner, "When will my heart be yours? I do not know!" The song is composed in the style of a Spanish

Habanera

In spite of all the admiration Carmen is piqued at the indifference of Corporal Don José and she begins to sing her song directly to him. She grows bolder with each verse and finally throws her flower straight at him. The crowd laughs and Carmen runs away.

The factory bell rings for the end of the noon recess, the workers go back into the building, and the crowd quickly disperses. Don José, left alone, looks at Carmen's flower lying on the ground, and, on a sudden impulse, he picks it up and places it inside his coat. As he does so he hears someone call his name and looks up to see his village sweetheart, Micaela.

"Micaela! What joy!" he cries. Micaela explains that she has come to bring him a message from his mother. "Tell me, how is she?" he asks, eagerly. Micaela answers his questions and gives him a letter and a purse containing money which Don José receives gratefully.

"There is something else your mother asked me to give you," Micaela says, hesitating and blushing a little. Then she adds softly, "She sent you a kiss by me." She kisses Don José gently on the forehead.

Deeply moved, he regards her fondly and returns her kiss. He then tells her to take his kiss, with his love, back to his mother. After a few more tender words Micaela leaves to return to the distant valley which Don José calls "home."

The Corporal has barely begun to read his mother's letter when disturbing shouts come from the factory and a crowd of excited workers rush out, all talking at once. Captain Zuniga and Don José ask for an explanation but have some trouble getting an answer. It finally becomes clear that Carmen and another girl have quarreled.

"Go in and see what the trouble is, Corporal," Zuniga commands, "and take two men with you." Don José goes into the factory with two soldiers and soon returns dragging Carmen by the arm. She is in a furious temper and looks much dishevelled.

"Captain, there has been a fight and one girl has been hurt," explains Don José to his superior officer.

"Who hurt her?" demands the Captain.

"Why, this girl," Don José replies, indicating Carmen.

"Do you hear that?" the Captain asks her sternly. "What have you to say?" Carmen looks at him impudently and then begins to sing, "Tra la, la, la, la, la . . . ."

"You may sing that song in jail," snaps the Captain and he orders Don José to bind her hands behind her back. All of this time Carmen continues her exasperating "tra la la la." This so angers Zuniga that he soon leaves her in Don José's care. The girls go back to work and the Corporal and Carmen are left alone in the square."

With her hands tied behind her Carmen sits down on the chair in front of the guardhouse where the Corporal has been sitting. "Where are you going to take me now?" she asks him.

"To jail. I obey orders," Don José replies in a curt tone.

Carmen coolly surveys him while he is looking in another direction and says, "This time you will disobey them . . . . because . . . . because you love me!"

"I? . . . . love you?" Don José demands, scornfully.

"Yes, José! That flower I gave to you today you have not thrown away. . . . . You feel its power!" she declares, a note of triumph in her voice.

"Stop talking to me," cries the Corporal. "Keep still!"

Carmen smiles, determined to follow up her advantage. Now she springs up and to hold Don José's attention, begins to dance and sing a Spanish

Seguidilla

During the song, in which Carmen sings of the good time to be had

at the Inn of Lillas Pastia on the outskirts of the city, Don José grows more and more disturbed. When she pauses, for sheer lack of breath, he cries out. "Do keep still! I told you not to talk to me."

"I did not speak to you," Carmen declares sweetly. "I only sang a song! I am thinking of a certain officer I know who . . . ." she waits, then says, "who loves me! Who knows? I might love him too!"

This is more than Don José can stand. "Carmen," he cries, "I am losing my senses. Tell me, if I let you escape, will you love me a little?"

"Yes," says Carmen simply as Don José loosens the cords that bind her hands. "Yes," she repeats in a caressing voice. "And at the Inn of Lillas Pastia we will dance the Seguidilla together!"

She quickly places her hands behind her and seats herself when Captain Zuniga emerges from the guardhouse with an order for her arrest in his hands. He gives the paper to Don José, telling him to be on the alert, and to see that his lovely prisoner does not escape. Carmen walks meekly in front of Don José as far as the bridge when she suddenly gives him a push. As he topples backward, she escapes across the bridge, laughing merrily.

A lively scene opens the next act. The Inn of Lillas Pastia is crowded with a gay throng, eating and drinking and dancing. There are many gypsies in the crowd, some of whom are playing the guitar or tambourine. Carmen joins in the gayety with a typical gypsy tune and soon many of the others sing with her.

Gypsy Song

At this point the entrance of Escamillo, the toreador, a victorious bull-fighter and a popular idol, causes great excitement. He receives the cheers of the crowd by bowing from right to left. He accepts a mug of wine from one of the men, and in response to their hearty welcome, drinks a toast to them all in a rousing song in which he relates some of his exploits in the bull ring.

Toreador's Song

Most of the girls try to catch the toreador's eye, but Carmen, after one flashing glance turns her back on him. This seeming indifference attracts the bull-fighter and as he continues his song, he advances toward Carmen and even attempts to embrace her, but she shakes him off. Escamillo takes his defeat smilingly and says he hopes for better luck next time. As he leaves, most of the crowd follow him.

Captain Zuniga has been in the crowd at the Inn. In spite of all the trouble Carmen has given him he cannot resist trying to win her favor. But she will have nothing to do with him. Her thoughts are for Don José who has suffered a term in military prison as punishment for allowing her to escape. She has learned that he has just been released and that he will come to her that night.

Several of Carmen's gypsy friends, members of a notorious band of smugglers, remain behind when the others leave. They talk to her and to two other gypsy girls, explaining that they need help in a new smuggling plot. To their astonishment Carmen, who has often helped them in the past, now refuses to go with them. She tells them that she is seriously in love and that her lover will soon be there.

At first they do not believe her and laugh uproariously, but she finally convinces them and hurries them away when she hears Don José's voice in the distance singing as he approaches the Inn.

"Oh, Carmen! . . . . You . . . . at last!" Don José cries when he sees her.

"You are just out of prison today?" she asks.

"Yes, I was there two months—all on account of you," he says tenderly, holding her in his arms.

"Did you mind?" she asks him.

"I would do much more than that for you," is his ardent reply. He places his sabre and helmet on a table and watches Carmen. She is exuberant as she seizes a pair of castenets and dances before him, crooning in time to the clicking rhythm.

Castenet Dance

la   la   la   la

la   la   la   la

"Stop for a moment, Carmen, stop!" Don José cries suddenly. "Don't you hear? The bugles are sounding retreat!" Carmen, after a momentary pause of surprise, gayly continues her fascinating dance.

Again Don José interrupts her, this time almost angrily. "Carmen, you don't understand," he cries. "It's the retreat! Time for me to go back to the barracks for the night!"

"Go back . . . . tonight?" Carmen is amazed. Then her quick temper rises and she bursts out, "Oh, how could I be so stupid! Here I have tried with all my might to please you. I have sung! . . . . I have danced! When 'ra-ta-ta-tat' . . . . a bugle call—and you're off!" By this time she is wild with anger and, flinging his helmet and sabre across the room, tells him to go.

"You are being cruel, Carmen," Don José tells her sadly. Carmen only mocks him and suggests that he hurry since he is so afraid of being late. She even tells him that she now believes that he does not love her at all.

"You really think I do not love you, Carmen?" he asks.

"Yes," she cries.

"Listen to me," he urges, but she only stops her ears, stamps her foot, and declares she will not listen to a single word.

"You must hear me," Don José insists. "I say you *must!*" he shouts, violently forcing her into a chair. Then he takes from an inside pocket the flower she playfully threw at him on the day of their first meeting. He shows it to her and then sings the Flower Song in which he reveals how deeply he loves her.

The Flower Song (La fleur que tu m'avais jetée)

Carmen listens unwillingly at first, but her manner gradually changes as she is convinced of Don José's sincerity. At the end of his song she asks him to prove his love—to give up his military life and flee with her to the mountains where she and the other gypsies live . . . . where there are no bugle calls to part lovers . . . . where all are free!

Don José, disconcerted by her wild ideas, is torn between his sense of duty and his mad infatuation. But his loyalty to duty prevails, and he is about to say farewell to Carmen when they are surprised by a loud knock at the locked door of the Inn. A moment later Captain Zuniga forces the door and enters. Seeing Don José, the Captain commands him to "get out!" but the Corporal refuses and seizing his sword, he defies his superior officer.

Carmen throws herself between the two angry men and her cries quickly bring her gypsy companions. They surround the Captain and force him to leave, while Carmen clings to Don José, who now realizes that he is disgraced and that he can never return to his old life. He consents to cast in his lot with the band of gypsies and they all hail him with a show of hearty comradeship and tell him what a life of "freedom" awaits him.

The next act shows a desolate pass in the mountains—the secret stronghold of the gypsy smugglers. Some of them are sleeping, wrapped in their long black cloaks, while others are seated by a fire and are chatting in low tones. Off to one side two pretty young girls are amusing themselves by telling their fortunes with a deck of cards. In the foreground, on the other side, sits Carmen. She leans against a rock and seems sullen and unhappy. Near her, resting on his carbine in a dejected attitude, stands Don José. He is now dressed in gypsy costume. For a long time nothing is said, while the following soft music is heard.

with stealth

Presently a smuggler appears, making his way up a mountain trail with a heavy pack on his shoulder. He is followed by another and another, and then they come in twos and threes, some carrying huge bales between them which they deposit on the ground. The other gypsies about the camp spring immediately to life and busy themselves.

Carmen and José have remained motionless. At last Carmen breaks the silence. "What are you thinking about?" she asks.

"I am thinking of a valley far below us where lives an aged woman who still believes me to be an honest fellow," says José.

"Who can that be?" Carmen asks with scorn in her voice.

"Ah, Carmen, do not laugh at me. It is my mother!"

"Go to her then, I know this life does not suit you." Her tone is cold.

"Go? . . . . Leave you?" José exclaims.

"Why not?" rejoins Carmen.

"Go away from you? It would be death!" But as Carmen remains silent, José remarks with bitterness, "Your silence tells me much." Unconsciously he places his hand on the long knife he carries in his belt, as do all the gypsy men.

"Kill me if you want to," she says calmly. "What difference would it make? I shall die when fate wills it." But José remains silent and motionless.

Carmen rises and saunters over to the two girls who are still laughing over their cards. After a time she seats herself and shuffles the cards for herself, only to find that again and again, she cuts to the ace of spades. "Spades! . . . . a grave! . . . . death! . . . . Well, let it come," she says.

Two of the gypsy look-outs come to announce that it is now time to cross the pass on a new raiding expedition. José is to remain behind to watch the bales of stolen goods which have just been brought in. The gypsies break camp in a hurry and soon all are ready to set out. As they pass, single file, up the mountain trail, Carmen throws a quick glance at José and then follows the others. José brings up the rear, walking slowly since he does not have to go any farther than the nearest look-out.

For a brief time the pass is deserted until the figure of a mountain guide is seen climbing down a rocky declivity from a direction opposite the one taken by the smugglers. He disappears in a turn of the trail, and Micaela comes in, looking about her fearfully. She is frightened and kneels down to pray for courage and that she may find José.

Micaela's Prayer

Suddenly she sees José on his rocky height, but just as she starts to hail him he raises his gun toward some unseen enemy and fires. Micaela is terrified and hides quickly behind a rock. Almost immediately Escamillo, the toreador, appears, the guide pointing out the way. He is followed by José.

Escamillo is holding his hat in his hand, examining it, and now he says, "Two inches lower and it would have been the end of me!"

"Who are you?" demands José.

"I am Escamillo, a toreador of Granada."

"Escamillo?" exclaims José. "The name is known to me. You are welcome, comrade, but what brings you here?"

"I am in love," explains Escamillo, "and he is a poor lover who will not risk his life to see his sweetheart."

"Do you expect to find her here?" José asks him.

"Yes," admits the toreador. "She is a gypsy . . . . charming!"

"What is her name?" José inquires.

"Carmen," Escamillo announces, proudly.

"Carmen!" José repeats the name with dismay in his voice.

"Yes. She had a soldier lover who became a deserter for her sake," Escamillo tells him, "but their love has died. Carmen is tired of him. Her fancy changes often."

"In spite of that, you love her?" demands José fiercely.

"Yes, I do," Escamillo admits.

"Anyone who takes away one of our gypsy girls must pay," cries José in threatening tones.

The toreador agrees. "Very well, I will pay."

"You will pay in knife-thrusts, do you understand?" José's manner is unmistakable.

"Oho! So then you are the soldier she loved!" Both men seize the long knives they carry at their belts, wind their serapes around their left arms and prepare to fight. At this point Carmen appears, followed by several of the gypsy men who have returned to find the cause of the shot. Carmen rushes between the angry rivals shouting "Stop! José!" The gypsies hold the two men apart and keep José from attacking the toreador in spite of all he can do. They allow Escamillo to depart, which he does leisurely, and not without ardent glances at Carmen which she returns.

"Carmen! Take care! I am tired of suffering," José warns her, but she only shrugs her shoulders and turns away.

"Come on, now. It is high time for all of us to be on our way," counsels one of the men, but an exclamation from one of the others arrests their attention. "There is someone moving about up there," he says. They run in the direction he points and bring in Micaela who is pale and trembling.

"A girl!" Carmen cries astonished.

"What a pleasant surprise," says one of the gypsies, but José can only groan. "Micaela, what has brought *you* here?"

"I come from your mother, Don José, who is weeping and waiting for you down there in the valley." Micaela says this with tears in her eyes.

"Go! Go! It would be better for you," urges Carmen.

"You want me to go?" José asks her.

"Yes," she says, "It would be better . . . ."

"Ha!" snarls José, interrupting her in jealous rage. "You want me to go so that you can follow your toreador. No, my fine traitress, I will not go and leave you free!"

"Listen to me," pleads Micaela. "Your mother needs you!" The others also urge José to go, but he is deaf to their words until Micaela tells him that his mother is dying.

"Then I must go at once!" José cries, "but we will see each other again," he says harshly to Carmen, and he and Micaela leave.

Carmen fails to show any outward emotion and does not speak. She walks to a high point and for a long time stands there motionless, looking after the two retreating figures which are slowly making their way down the side of the mountain.

Lively music is heard as a prelude to the rising of the curtain on the last act. The scene shows the open square in Seville in front of the great arena where the bull-fights are held. The gates are closed, but a happy throng is waiting for the picadors to appear. When they finally arrive, astride their white horses, they are greeted by cheers from the noisy crowd. A band begins to play and their favorite toreador, Escamillo, arrives with Carmen proudly clinging to his arm. She looks radiant in a white lace dress, a rare mantilla over her head, and red roses in her hair.

Slipping toward her from out of the crowd come Frasquita and Mercedes, two of Carmen's stanchest gypsy friends. Drawing her to one side they whisper a warning that José is lurking in the crowd and looks so desperate they are afraid he will harm her.

"Yes. I noticed him too, a moment ago," Carmen tells them. "I am no coward . . . . I shall stay right here and talk to him," and she refuses to listen to her friends' advice. Meanwhile Escamillo, after saying farewell, has gone into the arena with the crowd following him. Carmen waits outside, and now she and José face each other alone. He looks unkempt and desperate. They eye each other for a moment in a tense silence.

"So you are here," Carmen says in even tones.

"Yes," José's voice sounds muffled.

"I was warned that you were here," she tells him. "I was even told to fear for my life, but I am not a coward."

"I did not come to threaten you, Carmen. I am here only to beg you, to implore you, to come away with me, to begin a new life with me!" pleads José.

"What you ask is impossible." Carmen's voice is firm. "Between us, all is over." Deaf to José's frantic attempts to interrupt her she continues, "I know that my hour has come. Whether I live or die, I can never love you again." At these words José is transformed into wild fury, but sudden shouts from the arena arrest his attention.

As the cries grow into unmistakable cheers of victory for Escamillo, an exclamation of joy involuntarily breaks from Carmen's lips. This enrages José beyond endurance and as she moves toward the entrance of the arena, he springs in her path. "Where are you going?" he demands.

"Let me pass!" she cries.

"Are you going to him—the toreador?" His voice is thick with rage and he clutches her arm, roughly.

"Leave me alone," she warns, breaking away from him.

"You shall not go to him. I will not let you!" José is beside himself. "Once more, I ask you, Carmen, will you come with me?"

"No, No! Never!" she fairly screams at him. "Here . . . . see! . . . . the ring you gave me," and drawing it from her finger, she throws the ring to the ground with a gesture of disdain. "There! Take it!"

This so infuriates José that he draws his knife, and for the first time Carmen is frightened as she sees the wild look in his eyes. She attempts to evade him, but wherever she turns he blocks her path. Faster and faster she runs, first in this direction and then in that, but he is always before her with knife upraised. At last he catches her and stabs her. Carmen drops, mortally wounded. She makes one last effort to speak, but falls back, dead.

Just then the gates of the arena open and the gay crowd comes pouring out excited over the bull fight and the lastest victory of their popular idol, Escamillo. They are gradually silenced when they discover Carmen lying there and José standing over her as though stupefied. Suddenly he cries out, "I did it! I killed her! Oh, my beloved!" As he says these words he throws himself down beside her and breaks into uncontrollable sobs.

The crowd recoils. With one swift stroke, the tragedy has spoiled their festive day.

FAUST
or
THE FALSE CAVALIER
by CHARLES GOUNOD

Faust

AN old man is sitting at his desk lost in reverie and it is evident from his cramped position and the concentration of his pose that he has been sitting so for many hours. The room seems quite dark except for the mellow glow cast by a lamp which is burning low, and yet, by looking closely at the single window, a faint glimmer of gray light can be seen—the first approach of dawn.

This man, known as the mysterious Dr. Faustus, is a famous scholar whose life has been spent with books and this is apparent now for they fill the shelves which cover the walls of his study and are even stacked on the floor. The learning that Dr. Faustus has acquired through years of study has not brought him happiness and he has resolved to drink the poison in the cup before him. He is lonely and tired of life.

"I am old . . . . old," he mutters bitterly. "Nothing to live for now." Cursing his fate, he raises the fatal cup to his lips but suddenly stops and puts it down. As though to reprove his bitter words a gay song is heard beneath his window.

Street Song

The voices of young girls float up to him as they sing gayly on their way to a village festival. He leaves the poison untouched and hastens to fling wide the casements of his window. It is a bright clear morning for the sun is now fully risen. As he lingers to drink in the invigorating air, a group of young men pass down the street and they, too, are singing.

"Oh, to be young again," sighs Faust, for that is the name by which we shall know him better. "If I were young, I should not want to die."

"You may have your wish—at a price," a voice says. Faust turns, startled, wondering how anyone could have made his way through the locked door into this dingy tower room, but his visitor is one to whom locks and bolts are no hindrance. Standing in the gloom is a strange, spectre-like creature who sends a faint shiver down the scholarly spine of the aged doctor.

"You are not afraid of me, I hope?" the stranger asks.

"No," says Faust who has recognized his mysterious visitor as Mephistopheles—Satan, the Tempter. "No, I am not afraid." And a strange conversation ensues.

"You wished just now to be young again," observes Mephistopheles, for he has been able to read Faust's thoughts.

"You are right," replies Faust. "What would I not give to have back my youth, and with it to have vitality and ambition and joy in life!"

"I can help you," declares his visitor, "because you have cursed all the powers of good. But if you accept my help you must pay the price."

"What do you mean?" demands Faust.

"Promise to give me your real self—your soul," replies Mephistopheles, "and I will make you young again!"

"Is that possible?" exclaims Faust so dazzled by this prospect that even the loss of his immortal soul means nothing to him. "Is it true that you can give me back my youth?" Mephistopheles assures him of his power and the strange bargain is made.

"From now on I will be your servant and constant companion," declares Satan in a bland voice. "You need only to command me. But remember the hour of retribution!" he warns. "When that hour comes, you will find me your master!" Faust foolishly shrugs his shoulders at these ominous words. Already a feeling of youthful vigor is surging through him.

"Drink your poison now," commands Mephistopheles. "It is poison no longer but the magic of youth."

Faust obeys. At once he takes on the appearance of a handsome young man wearing the elegant costume of a cavalier. His mentor agrees to provide him with riches so that he may shine in any adventure he undertakes. Completely transformed, Faust dashes madly toward the door—and freedom! The whole world lies before him, and he can scarcely wait to leave his dingy room and its bitter memories.

As the curtain goes up on the next act, an entirely different stage picture is revealed. It is the public square of a quaint sixteenth century town, filled with a lively throng of men and women in colorful costumes. They are all dressed in their best and the orchestra is playing a merry tune. First one group and then another takes up the melody until at last they are all singing together.

FAUST
Festival Music (The Kermesse)

brightly

After a time the crowd disperses leaving only a few soldiers seated at a table in front of an inn which can be seen at one side of the stage. Now another soldier comes by, walking slowly, and fingering a religious medal which he wears on a ribbon around his neck. He is Valentine, brother of Marguerite one of the prettiest maidens in the town. She has given him this medal to wear as a charm to ward off danger in battle. The group of soldiers around the table, all friends of his, call out urging him to join them in a drink and teasing him for looking so serious.

Valentine replies that he has reason to be serious. He is not afraid to go to war since being a soldier is his business, but he cannot bear to leave his motherless sister, Marguerite, with no one to protect and care for her. At these words his friend Siebel steps forward. He has always loved Marguerite and he assures Valentine that he will give her a brother's protection. They shake hands on this and then join their friends. They drink and make merry together but Valentine cannot rid himself of misgivings, and gives heartfelt expression to his feelings in the following song.

Even bravest heart may swell, in the moment of farewell

moderato *mf*

Before the song is finished Valentine's friend, Wagner, interrupts. "We have had enough of this," he cries. "We are all growing sad from

67

listening to you. I will sing you a different song. Listen to this!" He bursts into a nonsensical ditty about a rat under a barrel, a popular song of the day. While he is still singing and the others are laughing at the words or joining in the chorus, an unknown gentleman saunters toward them. He bears himself with an air of proud elegance and interrupts Wagner's vocal effort somewhat rudely, saying, "I will sing you something more clever!"

Surprised and a little annoyed by this intrusion, they meet his remark with silence. Then, thinking better of it, they invite him to go ahead. Without waiting to be urged further the stranger begins his song which he calls *The Calf of Gold*. The words say that the world bows down to the power of money and that greed for wealth makes rascals of most people. The singer ends up with the line, "And Satan leads them all a dance."

"What a jolly song," one of the young men cries. Laughing and applauding, the soldiers gather around him. Valentine alone stands aside, muttering to himself, "Queer, but this fellow gives me a most uncomfortable feeling."

Mephistopheles, for it is he, asks them to join him in a toast. As they do this he gains their confidence further by pretending that he can tell their fortunes. Turning to Siebel he takes his hand and looking at it, says, "Never again touch any flowers for they will wither in your hand." As Siebel looks up surprised, the Devil adds significantly, "This means, no more bouquets for Marguerite."

"How dare you mention my sister's name," cries Valentine in sudden anger, but Mephistopheles merely laughs at him and in a sneering voice boldly proposes a toast, "To Marguerite!" This is more than Valentine can stand and he quickly draws his sword. At once his mysterious adversary marks a circle about himself with the tip of his own weapon. As Valentine advances he finds his sword powerless and in another moment it breaks in two.

The young soldier and his friends stand aghast. They sense the presence of an evil power and, moved by one thought, they draw their swords and turn the cross-shaped hilts toward Valentine's opponent. At the sign of the cross the bravado of the Evil One crumbles and he backs away helpless before the symbol of good. Replacing his sword in its scabbard he lamely mutters, "We will meet again, Gentlemen," and turns away. Strangely moved by this incident, Valentine and his friends silently go off in another direction.

The square once more slowly fills with people who walk about, talking and laughing with each other. Faust, now a rich young cavalier, soon appears among them. He is joined by Mephistopheles whom he draws aside. Faust then reminds him of his promise to arrange a meeting with a certain girl—who turns out to be Marguerite, Valentine's sister.

The Devil assures him that he will keep his promise and tells Faust to mingle with the crowd if he wants to see Marguerite who will soon come across the square on her way home from church. "You may even have a chance to speak to her," suggests Mephistopheles. Faust watches eagerly for a glimpse of Marguerite while the Devil wanders about among the people, unnoticed by them because he has made himself invisible. The music turns into a lively waltz and soon all the people start to dance. They whirl faster and faster, quite unaware that they are led by the invisible presence of His Satanic Majesty.

Mephisto Waltz

lively

Before long Marguerite crosses the square, demurely carrying a prayer book. By her side is Martha, an elderly neighbor, who takes a good-natured interest in the motherless girl. Marguerite wears a light blue dress which sets off her fair complexion and her blond hair hangs down her back in two thick braids in the fashion of the day. Faust, seeing her face to face, is overwhelmed by her beauty and charm and boldly steps up to her, asking if he may escort her home. Some of the girls standing nearby laugh and titter. Marguerite refuses his advances and goes on her way although she is secretly flattered at his evident admiration. Just before she passes out of sight, she turns to look again at her unexpected admirer and meets Faust's ardent glance still fixed upon her.

The first scene of the next act, one of the most beautiful in the opera, shows the garden in front of Marguerite's modest home. As the curtain rises the garden appears deserted, but it is not long before Siebel comes in. It is his custom to bring flowers to Marguerite, his childhood friend, and he now stops to pick some but pauses in dismay as the flowers wither at his touch. He remembers the ominous prophecy made by the stranger and to break the evil spell—for Siebel is sure it is evil—he dips his hand in holy water at a small shrine in the wall of the garden. Again Siebel picks the flowers and is overjoyed to find that, this time, they remain fresh and lovely! Overcome with thoughts of love for Marguerite, he sings the following song asking the flowers to "speak" for him.

Siebel's Song

Siebel now places his simple love-offering on the doorstep where Marguerite will find it and leaves. He has scarcely closed the garden gate behind him when Faust, with Mephistopheles at his heels, enters from another direction. The Devil examines Siebel's humble gift with a shrug of the shoulders and then throws it down contemptuously, while Faust begs to be left alone in the garden so that he may speak of his love freely. After a time Mephistopheles goes, but not without backward glances of cynical amusement as he takes his departure.

Left alone, Faust gazes longingly at the home of his adored Marguerite and then sings one of the most touching and famous songs in the opera.

All hail, thou dwelling pure and lowly

While he is still lingering there, his love song apparently unheard, Mephistopheles returns, bringing with him a casket of jewels which is to be Faust's gift to Marguerite. The casket is placed near Siebel's nosegay and Faust unwillingly yields to Mephistopheles's command that they take their departure. When the garden gate opens again it is to admit Marguerite, who walks in slowly, evidently in a pensive mood. Seating herself on a bench near which her spinning-wheel stands, she rather absent-mindedly begins to spin and to sing in a low voice a song familiar in that day—*The King of Thule*.

Every now and then she breaks off her song to think about the handsome and admiring young cavalier who had spoken to her in the square. She recalls how excited she was at his attention and admits it, saying to herself, "I know I blushed. How silly of me!"

After a time Marguerite grows restless and gets up to walk about the garden. On the doorstep she discovers Siebel's bouquet. She picks it up somewhat casually murmuring "Poor, faithful boy!", then drops it in her amazement at seeing the jewel casket. The temptation to open this mysterious box is the greatest that has ever come to Marguerite. It would be so easy, for lying beside it, invitingly, is a tiny golden key! But she hesitates for she feels sure that there must be some mistake. She looks again. There it is . . . . surely, surely, it would not be very wrong to unlock it and take just one look.

She finally obeys this natural impulse and is struck with bewilderment at what she sees, for the casket is filled with the most beautiful jewels imaginable. With cries of delight she takes out a bracelet and places it on her arm, holding it up to admire it. Then she tries on a brilliant ring and finds that it just fits her finger. She grows more and more excited and, plunging both hands into the mass of dazzling gems, draws forth a magnificent necklace which she hurriedly clasps around her neck. Then she adds more bracelets and rings and a pair of earrings —there seems to be no end to what the casket holds!

Gazing at her image in a mirror which is included in the casket's contents, she dances about in childish glee. "Oh, if only the handsome stranger could see me now!" she cries and sings the famous

Jewel Song

Old Martha comes to find out what Marguerite is doing and pauses in surprise at the sight of her young friend who is still wearing the jewels. Marguerite tells Martha that there must be some dreadful mistake and that the box could not be meant for her, but she confesses that, having found the casket on her doorstep, she could not resist trying on the beautiful jewelry.

"Not meant for you?" exclaims Martha. "Don't be silly! Of course it is meant for you! I would not be a bit surprised if . . . ." but Martha does not finish for at that moment a courtly gentleman comes down the garden path, closely followed by the young cavalier who had spoken to Marguerite in the public square. The gentleman, bowing low, addresses Martha as "Dame Schwertlein", (which is her married name) and offers the hope that he and his young friend, indicating Faust, are not intruding. Martha, slightly embarrassed, drops a courtesy and assures the visitors they are welcome. Marguerite is quite distressed and hastily takes off the jewelry.

His Satanic Majesty, in the guise of a noble cavalier, proceeds to flatter silly old Martha by his attentions and leads her to a remote corner of the garden in order to give Faust his longed-for opportunity to talk with Marguerite alone.

Faust is at first unsuccessful in his advances. Marguerite is shy and a little afraid of him, but he gradually breaks down her reserve and explains that the casket of jewels is but a trifling gift from him as an expression of his admiration. Marguerite is pleased and flattered, and when he ventures to tell her that he loves her, she admits that she has loved him, too, since the moment of their first meeting. This makes Faust supremely happy and he and Marguerite sing a beautiful love duet.

When the curtain rises on the third act, some time has elapsed since the garden scene in which Marguerite tells Faust that she loves him. At first, after her avowal, Marguerite has been the envy of all the village for having attracted such a rich admirer. As time passes, however, it becomes evident that Faust does not intend to marry Marguerite. Finally

he heartlessly leaves her and the envious chatter of Marguerite's friends turns to jeers and cruel gossip. Only the faithful Siebel comes to console her and to assure her that he, at least, still loves her as he always has. But this is poor comfort for Marguerite who is heart-broken.

The scene shows the interior of a church where Marguerite is praying. She is filled with remorse and haunted by superstitious terror. She imagines that she sees the Devil lurking behind a pillar, smirking at her, and thinks she hears a voice saying that her sins will never be forgiven. This nightmare vision is too much for her overwrought nerves, and she falls senseless before the altar.

Now again there is a complete change of scene which shows the sunny public square where the buildings are decorated with flags and banners, and the people gathered there seem to be in holiday mood. They move about restlessly as though waiting for some important event.

The cause of all this excitement is soon apparent for rousing military music is heard and the soldiers come marching proudly down the street.

Soldiers' March and Chorus

The war is over and one of the happiest of the returning soldiers is Valentine, Marguerite's brother. He greets Siebel and other friends and acquaintances joyfully, and then hurries along, eager to be welcomed by his sister. Siebel attempts to detain him, to give him some hint or explanation of his sister's misery, but Valentine is too impatient to listen and enters his home in ignorance of Marguerite's unhappy state. It is from her own lips that he learns her sad story.

Hours have passed and as the darkness falls, Faust and his inevitable companion, Mephistopheles, can be seen stealing toward Marguerite's home. Mephistopheles is carrying a guitar. He tells Faust that he is a fool to return to "this silly girl", but Faust has been unable to forget Marguerite and has come back with the hope of making amends for his

74

cruel desertion. He is too much of a coward, however, to go boldly into the house. While he is hesitating Mephistopheles suggests, with a sneer, "Since you do not dare to open the door to let her know we are here, I will sing a song to your lady love that will waken her."

To Faust's intense indignation, the Devil sings a cruel and insulting serenade to an accompaniment on his guitar and ends up with a burst of heartless laughter.

Mephistopheles's Serenade

This outburst arouses Marguerite's brother, who now appears in the door, blazing with anger. Seeing the two men he demands which one was his sister's lover. Learning that it was Faust, Valentine draws his sword to slay him. The contest is brief for Valentine drops to the ground, fatally wounded.

Faust and his evil companion slink away as the people, roused by the fighting, come running from all directions. Marguerite, too, has been awakened and dashes out to her dying brother, reaching his side only in time to hear his last words.

Faust, already filled with remorse for his cowardly desertion of Marguerite, now faces the realization that he has killed her brother and he cannot forgive himself. But Mephistopheles has no patience with such feelings and in order to distract his companion and help him to forget, he leads him into novel and exciting adventures.

First he drags Faust to the edge of a crater on a mountain peak and shows him the fiery pits of hell where weird goblins and hideous creatures dance in the flickering shadows cast by red and green lights.

Then, to give his victim further evidence of his power, Mephistopheles transports Faust to a magnificent banquet hall in a stately palace, wonderful beyond anything human eyes have seen. Here are beautiful women, famous in history,—Cleopatra, Lais, Helen of Troy, and many others. A great feast is in progress and, at the imperious command of Satan, Faust is made a welcome guest. But even in these distracting surroundings

Faust cannot keep the thought of Marguerite from his memory. Suddenly he sees a vision of her . . . . she is ill and dying! Crying out that he must go to her, Faust starts up and dashes from the magic banquet hall. Mephistopheles follows him, jeering with amused contempt.

Meanwhile Marguerite, stricken with grief and fear, has killed her child. Now, in the closing scene of the opera, she is in prison. It is dawn and she is awaiting her execution. Faust and Mephistopheles, having ridden hard all night, reach the prison and enter the cell where Marguerite lies huddled on a bed of straw, asleep.

Faust rushes to her, awakens her with every expression of endearment, and explains that he has come to help her to escape. She starts up, but seems to be dazed and does not understand him. Deeply moved, Faust implores her frantically to come away with him, explaining that they must hurry or the jailor will discover them. Mephistopheles, standing in the background, adds his urgent words to those of Faust, but to their intense surprise Marguerite does not heed them. She appears strangely remote and with an unearthly calm resists Faust's excited efforts to lead her to freedom and happiness. Instead she gazes upward where she imagines that she sees "angels of light" who beckon to her and assure her of divine forgiveness.

The music beautifully describes her state of mind. There is the sound of the heavenly choir mingled with Faust's urgent pleadings, the dark mutterings of Mephistopheles, and the exalted voice of Marguerite as her prayers are answered. She rises and stands motionless with her arms upraised, gazing at the celestial vision. . . . .

Suddenly her manner changes, and for the first time she seems completely aware of the presence of her false lover. Turning to Faust she exclaims, "Why do you look at me so? Go away! I cannot bear the sight of you!" With these words of reproach she falls dead.

Faust cries out in dismay and Mephistopheles gloatingly mutters, "Now his soul is mine!" At these words they disappear and angel voices are heard singing of Marguerite's redemption.

IL TROVATORE
or
THE TROUBADOUR
by GIUSEPPE VERDI

Il Trovatore

WHEN Columbus sailed away upon his memorable voyage of discovery which brought him to America in 1492, the southern part of Spain was rich with the art and culture of the Middle Ages. Churches and splendid palaces ornamented the cities and the court of Ferdinand and Isabella moved in luxurious grandeur.

At the same time, life in the northern provinces of Spain was harsh, thrilling and adventurous. The castles were not as impressive or showy as those to the south of them, yet the nobles had their court life, their tournaments, and their troubadours in spite of almost continuous warfare. Lasting peace was impossible to these knights of Arragon and Biscay, so fierce was the hatred and rivalry which existed between them.

Many knights of that period, when not fighting, pursued the gentler arts of poetry and music, and many of them became as noted for their achievements in these pursuits as for deeds of valor. These troubadours traveled from court to court, serenading fair ladies or performing brilliant feats at arms in the tournaments staged in their honor. Their fame spread from province to province and many hearts fluttered and sighed because of the mystery and romance inspired by these gallant knights.

The story of this opera brings us first to the Castle of Aliaferia, belonging to the reigning Prince of Arragon, and deals with the adventures of the Lady Leonora, one of the ladies-in-waiting to the royal Princess.

In a recent tournament, Leonora has had the honor of crowning the victor, an unknown troubadour, and has thought of him ever since as her perfect knight. The Troubadour has thought her his perfect lady and, still hiding his identity, has dared to steal into the palace gardens more than once for a clandestine meeting. By doing so, he has ventured into the enemy's domain. Moreover, in this court of Arragon there is a powerful young noble, Count di Luna, who is likewise a suitor for the Lady Leonora's hand.

When the curtain rises on the first act, it reveals a vestibule in the Castle of Aliaferia in Arragon. It is near midnight, and Ferrando, elderly Captain of the Prince's Guards and also in the service of the Count di Luna, is entertaining a group of soldiers of the night watch with gossip of the court. When they appear sleepy he warns them to remain wide awake since, at any moment, the Count may pass that way to walk beneath the balcony of the Lady Leonora as has lately become his custom.

"It is jealousy makes him do that," observes one of the soldiers.

"Yes, that unknown troubadour who serenades her almost nightly is proving a serious rival," agrees Ferrando.

"If you wish us to stay wide awake, tell us again the story of Garzia, the Count's younger brother," they urge Ferrando. Although the tale is not new to them they are thrilled by its horrors and crowd about the old retainer in order not to lose a single word. With an air of great importance the talkative old Captain begins his story:

The former Count di Luna had two sons, the present Count, and a younger brother named Garzia. When the latter was still an infant in his cradle, his nurse awoke one morning to see an old gypsy standing by the crib gazing intently at the child. Terrified, she drove away the old hag who insisted that she had come only to tell the child's fortune. From that day the baby boy appeared to sicken, and all were sure an evil spell had been cast upon him. The Count di Luna ordered the gypsy to be burned at the stake as a witch, but to the very end the old woman protested her innocence. The gypsy's daughter, maddened by her mother's horrible fate, swore to be avenged. One day she managed to reach the cradle of the infant Garzia, snatch up the child and carry him away. None knew whether he had been killed or whether he still lived for he was not seen again. The Count, before he died, solemnly charged his son, the present Count, ever to be on the look-out for the gypsy in order that she might be apprehended and punished. The old Count never gave up his belief that his second son lived and he further charged the young Count not to relinquish the search for his brother.

"That vicious gypsy!" cries Ferrando in wrathful tones. "I would know her even now, if I saw her, that wicked daughter of a witch!"

"It would be a just deed to kill her," declares one of the soldiers.

"The witch is sometimes seen even now in various shapes," others assert, repeating a popular superstition.

"Some have seen her on the house-tops," whispers one soldier looking about him fearfully.

"Sometimes she appears in the shape of a vampire," says another.

"She flits about at night like a crow of ill-omen," offers a third soldier.

"She has been heard to utter hideous screams at midnight," observes the one who had spoken first. At that very moment, a bell tolls twelve.

Muttering curses on the dread witch, they rise and file out to change the watch, as thoroughly terrified by the tale as if they had just heard it for the first time.

The next scene the same night brings us into the palace gardens. The Lady Leonora is restlessly pacing back and forth and with her is her faithful companion, Inez, who now begs her mistress to return within. Leonora refuses even though Inez tells her that the Princess awaits her.

"Must another night pass without my seeing him?" she exclaims impatiently.

"The love you bear this mysterious knight is dangerous," warns Inez. "Tell me again how it all began."

"At the tournament!" explains Leonora who delights in re-living the experience. "He came—an unknown knight—clad in black armor, a sable plume waving from his helmet, but no device upon his shield. He entered the lists without disclosing his identity and right royally he fought until he had overthrown all our knights. . . . . Then on his brow I placed the wreath of victory!" She pauses for a moment, exulting in the memory, then her voice becomes reminiscent. "War came to divide Arragon and Biscay, and I saw him not again. Time passed and I feared he had forgotten me!" Lost in thought for a moment she then continues to tell with animation what Inez already knows only too well—that one night, when all were sleeping, the song of a troubadour was heard beneath her windows. He was her unknown knight.

"What you tell me fills me with dread," declares Inez. "You do not know this stranger!"

"Hah! Have no fear!" laughs Leonora.

"I wish he had never seen you. Do try to forget him!" urges her companion.

"Forget him? Never!" cries her mistress. "You have no idea how much I love him," and she tells of her devotion in the following song.

Ah! no, 'twere vain concealing

They wait a little longer and then, since the troubadour has not appeared, the Lady Leonora slowly and reluctantly ascends the steps to the palace, followed by Inez. Almost immediately the Count appears, and looking up at Leonora's window where a light is burning, expresses his longing for her. His romantic thoughts are interrupted by the soft tinkling music of a lute.

"The troubadour!" the Count exclaims in an undertone and hides himself. The Unknown Knight, who still conceals his identity behind a visored cap, now appears under the balcony. He can sing as gallantly as he can fight and he begins his serenade, accompanying himself on the lute.

The Count, withdrawn into the shadows, listens to the song of his rival with growing resentment. The Lady Leonora also has heard the song for she can be seen hastily descending the marble steps leading into the gardens. Mistaking the dark figure of the Count for that of the Troubadour she rushes into his arms with a cry of delight and words of endearment. It is now the Troubadour's turn to be dismayed and the word "traitress" springs from his lips. Just at this moment the moon breaks through the clouds and Leonora sees her terrible mistake. Frantically she throws herself at the feet of her Unknown Knight who raises her gently to take her in his arms and forgive her. The Count, enraged, draws his sword and demands that the Troubadour reveal himself.

"Alas! O woeful hour!" cries Leonora wringing her hands for she knows that danger threatens her knight.

The Troubadour promptly raises his visor and says, "Behold me, then. I am Manrico of Urgel, a Knight of Biscay."

"You madman!" snarls the Count. "You, one of Urgel's men, dare to show yourself here?"

"I do," is Manrico's haughty reply. "Call your guards! You can destroy me but you cannot make me fear you!"

"Your doom is near. Draw then!" challenges the Count. Both draw their weapons, but the Lady Leonora flings herself between them, crying hysterically, "Hear me! Stay!" The two knights, sworn enemies with hatred enhanced by jealousy, refuse to yield to her pleadings. In spite of all she can do they shake her off and then withdraw to a more secluded part of the gardens, their swords held aloft. Leonora falls senseless to the ground.

Several months have elapsed when the next act takes place. The curtain rises to show a straggling gypsy settlement in the mountains of Biscay.

It is dawn and a number of gypsies are scattered about. Some sit in groups and talk in low tones, others, wrapped in their mantles, are stretched out still fast asleep.

Seated near the fire is an aged gypsy known fondly by all the tribe as "Mother" Azucena. Manrico, wrapped in his long black cloak and with his helmet at his feet, is resting near her. He is gazing intently at his sword which he holds in his hand. Neither he nor the Count di Luna had come to serious harm in the duel they fought so fiercely in the castle gardens. Manrico, however, had successfully escaped from the enemy's domain but he had not been able to see Lady Leonora again. During the intervening months, the border war between Arragon and Biscay has broken out anew. At the battle of Pellila, Manrico has been severely wounded by the Count's men but Azucena has nursed him back to health with tender care. Manrico is devoted to this old gypsy and looks upon her as his mother for she has raised him from infancy and is devoted to him.

His thoughts turn now to Leonora as they often do. He is dreaming of the happy time when the fortunes of war will enable him to see her again, for he has never given up the hope of winning her.

As the dawn brightens the gypsies begin to stir and soon some of the men gather about the anvils to begin the day's work. They sing at their task and merrily strike the anvils in time to the tune they are singing. Before long the women join in the chorus.

Anvil Chorus

All this time old Azucena has been sitting motionless, staring before her as though seeing a vision. She often does this, and now she begins to mutter in a strange, low voice. The gypsies cease their singing to gather around her. Manrico, too, listens.

Fierce Flames are Soaring (Stride la vampa)

Azucena sings of roaring flames, of a human shape writhing in agony at a fiery stake in the midst of jeers of derision. "Your morning song is a sad one, Mother," remarks one of the men.

"It is sad," admits Azucena, "but sadder still is the story I must ever remember." Then turning to Manrico she says in a tone of mysterious import, "Vengeance! I must have vengeance!"

"Again those mysterious words," mutters Manrico to himself. "I wonder what is in her mind."

"Come, men!" shouts the gypsy leader. "It is day and time to descend upon the nearest village to forage for food." Singing light-heartedly, they are soon on their way, but Manrico remains near Azucena who has again fallen into silence.

"None can hear us now, Mother," he says to her. "You have so often hinted at some terrible thing—a disaster which happened to you. Tell me about it."

"It is the story of my mother's cruel death," Azucena replies in a smothered voice. Then after a pause she relates in awful detail the story of this death. She tells him that her mother was burned at the stake and that she was innocent of the crime they charged her with, that of casting an evil spell upon Garzia, the infant son of the Count di Luna. It is the same story that Ferrando has related to the horrified soldier guards at the beginning of the opera.

"I swore revenge!" cries Azucena bitterly, "because they killed my mother."

"What did you do?" asks Manrico.

"I stole the child of that cruel noble," cries Azucena almost triumphantly, "and I, too, had a fire kindled!"

"Mother! Revenge by fire?" gasps Manrico shrinking from her.

"With the whimpering child in my arms, pity came into my heart," Azucena continues, "but of a sudden a dark cloud came over my spirit.

Again I heard my mother shrieking. Blindly I reached for the infant where it lay beside my own and hurled it into the flames! Too late I saw that I had killed my own child. The other remained!" She pauses, her voice choking.

"What are you telling me, Mother!" cries Manrico horrified. "Oh, what a dreadful deed! Say no more," he begs, as Azucena falls back exhausted by her wild emotion.

"Was I that child? Tell me, are you not my mother?"

"I *am* your mother!' asserts Azucena hastily. "What did I say? What makes you ask?" She speaks rapidly. "When that hour of horror comes before me I seem to lose my mind . . . . Say! Speak! Have I not always been a loving parent to you?"

"Indeed you have," responds Manrico gratefully. "And yet . . . . and yet . . . ." he muses. "It comes to me now. . . . At Pellila, before I was wounded, I had that accursed di Luna at my mercy, yet as I stood over him with my uplifted sword a heavenly warning came to me. 'End this feud' the voice seemed to say, and I spared him."

"But he did not spare you later," cries Azucena bitterly. "He almost killed you. I! . . . . I, nursed you back to health. If you meet him again show him no mercy I beg you, my son!"

The sound of a horn is heard and there is an answering signal. Manrico springs up. "It must be Ruiz," he cries. (Ruiz is one of his loyal followers.) "Perhaps he brings news of new warfare!" Not Ruiz, but a messenger from him enters bearing a letter which Manrico reads quickly.

"Our men have taken the Fortress of Castellor. The Prince orders that you come at once to defend it unless your wounds are still unhealed. And know you, too, that the Lady Leonora, deceived by news of your death, is this day entering a convent."

"Oh, cruel fate!" cries Manrico for the news of Leonora overshadows all else. Then, turning to the messenger, he commands, "Bring my horse at once!"

"Manrico, what is it?" says Azucena watching him. Manrico, overwhelmed by the thought of losing Leonora, hastily puts on his helmet and makes ready to leave. "Where are you going?" she demands.

"To Castellor! To . . . . I cannot stop for words," he cries impatiently. "I must go at once."

"Listen! Your wounds are not yet healed," remonstrates Azucena. "I will not let you go!"

"I must! I must!" shouts Manrico. "Mother, farewell!" And he storms away although Azucena still vainly strives to hold him back.

It is night. The cloisters of a convent near Castellor are visible through the trees. The Count di Luna enters stealthily with Ferrando and a number of his followers. "All is quiet. We are safe," whispers the Count.

"This is a daring adventure, my lord," warns Ferrando.

"Not too daring for one who has been crossed in love!" declares the Count who is determined to carry off Leonora before she takes her vows at the altar.

Left alone, he dreams of a blissful future with Leonora.

In the light of her sweet glances (Il balen del suo sorriso)

The convent bell tolls and singing can be heard within. The Count and his men conceal themselves to await Leonora's coming.

She soon arrives with her attendants. Inez walks beside her weeping. "Why do you weep?" asks Leonora.

"Oh, dear mistress, does this not mean that we shall part forever?" sobs Inez.

"Kind heart, forget your grief," replies Leonora gently. "For me there is no hope or joy in life. Through years of penitence I trust to be united with my beloved in heaven." She is about to proceed to the entrance of the convent when the Count springs in her path. "Never!" he cries.

"Merciful heavens! Why are you here, rash man?" Leonora cries.

"To make you mine," declares the Count. At these words the tall figure of Manrico steps between the Count and Leonora. In the general consternation, for they all believe they are seeing a ghost, Leonora is the first to find her voice.

"Can I believe my eyes?" she cries, while the Count mutters, "Can the dead escape?" Manrico reassures Leonora by clasping her in his arms and Ruiz now joined by Manrico's men cries, "Long live Urgel!"

"Heaven has heard your prayers," Leonora's attendants exclaim joyfully gathering around her. At the same time the Count's followers forcibly hold back their leader as he attempts to reach Manrico and kill him. "This is madness," they tell him as they disarm him and lead him away.

"Fortune favors you at last, my lord," says Ruiz as Manrico proudly gives his hand to Leonora and takes her away to Castellor.

The next scene is the armed camp of the Arragon forces, commanded by the Count di Luna, as the banner floating from a tent in the foreground indicates. The Fortress of Castellor can be seen in the distance. The foreground is filled with soldiers, some playing dice, some polishing their weapons, others on sentinel duty. A band of cross-bowmen files across the stage at the back.

"Those are troops sent to reenforce us," remarks one of the soldiers.

"We are to storm the fortress at dawn," announces Ferrando. The Count enters and looks angrily in the direction of Castellor.

"In the arms of my rival," he mutters. "Hateful thought!" A confused noise without disturbs him and several soldiers enter, dragging a struggling gypsy woman between them.

"What does this mean?" demands the Count.

"My lord, we found this woman on the outskirts of the camp. Her actions were suspicious. She tried to run away but we captured her, thinking her a spy."

"Release me, you madmen!" Azucena, for it is she, glares at the soldiers who have bound her hands behind her.

"Come here," orders the Count. "Answer me and tell the truth. Where were you going just now?"

"Nowhere in particular," is her reply. "It is a gypsy custom to wander about."

"Where do you come from?" asks the Count, and when she replies, "Biscay," an exclamation escapes him and Ferrando looks at her searchingly.

"I lived there contentedly enough," says Azucena, "until my only son left me. Now I am wandering in search of him."

"Have you lived long in those mountains?" asks the Count in a grave voice. "Did you ever hear anything of the infant boy stolen from his father's castle about twenty years ago?" Ferrando notes Azucena's evident fright while the Count continues, "That infant was my brother!" A long "Ah-h-h-h-h-h!" escapes Azucena although she quickly recovers herself and makes an evident attempt to speak carelessly as she continues.

"The story concerns me not," she says. "Release me!" Ferrando now steps forward and openly accuses her as the gypsy who stole Garzia, while Azucena vigorously affirms her innocence. At the Count's order, the guards surround her and she cries in desperation, "O Manrico, my son! Help your unhappy mother!"

"Can it be true—she, Manrico's mother! And in my power!" The Count's voice carries a note of triumph as he signals the guards to drag off the prisoner, and then re-enters his tent with Ferrando.

The next scene shows a beautiful room in the Fortress of Castellor, with a balcony at the back. Leonora is in a long white satin dress. Hurried preparations have been made for her immediate marriage to Manrico and they are discussing their plans when Ruiz enters in great excitement bringing the news of Azucena's capture. He also says that the Count is preparing to have her burned as a witch. Manrico springs to the balcony which gives him a view of the enemy's camp.

"You are trembling. What is it?" cries Leonora who has followed him.

"It is my mother they are torturing," he tells her.

"Your mother! What are you saying?" exclaims Leonora in consternation.

"It must not go on. Ruiz . . . . our men! Collect them quickly. To the foe at once!" he shouts madly. A few quick commands and the soldiers enter, orders are given, and they rush away, Manrico leading them.

The scene of the next act is a towered wing of the Castle of Aliaferia. The windows are heavily barred. Here Manrico is imprisoned, condemned to die, and with him, also awaiting death, is Azucena. Manrico's impetuous sortie from the impregnable Fortress of Castellor to save the old gypsy has resulted in defeat for him and his men. He has been brought to this stronghold to await death.

Leonora, distracted and broken-hearted, has tried in every way to reach him. Now a desperate plan has brought her here at the dead of night—a plan which may bring freedom to Manrico but which may cost her her life. Ruiz, who has been her guide, points to the tower and says, "This is the place. They brought him here. An unhappy day for us all!"

"Go, now," commands Leonora, "and do not fear for me. It may be that I can save him." Ruiz leaves without delay for the neighborhood of this castle in Arragon is not an inviting spot to a warrior of Biscay. "Why should I fear?" Leonora says to herself. "I have my protector with me," and she looks long and earnestly at a jewelled ring she wears.

A bell tolls and voices off-stage can be heard intoning the solemn *Miserere.* Leonora is tortured anew by these "voices of terror".

Leonora's voice

Suddenly the Troubadour can be heard from the tower singing of his undying love for Leonora.

The Troubadour's Farewell

The *Miserere* is heard again, but the Troubadour continues his sad song while Leonora mingles her voice with his, giving frantic expression to her feelings.

A door opens and the Count steps forth, followed by some of his men. Leonora quickly conceals herself but listens intently as the Count gives his orders. "Mark me," he says to the guards, "here on this spot, at dawn, you will behead him and burn his mother at the stake." When the men re-enter the tower the Count mutters, "I am led to this revengeful act by the loss of the woman I love. I have searched for her in vain. O cruel one, where are you?"

"Here, before you!" announces Leonora stepping forward.

"You . . . here?" cries the Count in wonder.

"You see me," Leonora says disdainfully.

"Why did you come here?" demands the Count. "How have you dared?"

"I have come to beg for mercy." Leonora's voice is tense.

"You are mad!" exclaims the Count angrily. "How can you ask me to take pity on my rival?" Leonora throws herself at his feet, imploring him to let her die in place of Manrico, but this only goads the Count to wilder fury. The more she pleads, the more cruel are his retorts and at last, beside himself with rage, he turns to leave her.

Now Leonora clings to him. "You *must* listen to me," she cries wildly.

"Never! Nothing on earth can buy his freedom now that I have him in my power," says the Count.

"Yes, there is one price—one price only, you will not refuse." She extends her right hand toward the Count and utters the single word, "Myself!"

"Do you mean that?" demands the Count.

"You have my promise," is her response. She demands, now, that the Count unbar the gates to the tower so that she may go to Manrico and tell him herself that he is free. "Then I will be yours," she adds quietly.

"You swear it?" asks the Count, still unbelieving.

"I swear it!" Leonora speaks the words with a strange exaltation, then presses the ring to her lips. The Count gives the order to his guards and Leonora disappears into the tower.

The last scene shows the gloomy dungeon where Manrico and Azucena are held prisoners. The old woman lies on a pallet of straw, apparently asleep. Manrico sits near her, his head in his hands. As she turns restlessly he speaks. "Mother, you are not sleeping."

"In vain I try," she sighs. "This air is suffocating me."

"If I could only set you free," groans Manrico.

"I shall soon die," she says and then starts up in terror. "What is that noise?"

"Nothing, Mother, nothing." Manrico tries to sooth her, but the old gypsy begins to pace the floor. Again that vision comes before her eyes . . . . a burning stake! She cries out again and again in a mad frenzy until she falls exhausted into Manrico's arms. He leads her back to her straw bed and begs her to compose herself. At his soothing words she gradually grows quiet, and at last, between sleeping and waking, she sings softly of going home to the mountains in Biscay which she loves. After a time Manrico, too, takes up the refrain and they sing together until Azucena sleeps.

Home to Our Mountains

The door opens and Leonora enters. Manrico can scarcely believe it is she. In breathless haste she tells him that he is free. "Go! At once! I have come to save you!" she cries.

"To save me?" asks Manrico, not understanding. "You are going with me?" he asks; but Leonora, crying "No! No!" tries frantically to push him toward the door. Suddenly his suspicions are aroused and he accuses Leonora of having been unfaithful to him. At this she throws herself into his arms and confesses that she has taken poison, carried in her ring, in order to outwit the Count.

As she makes this confession, the Count, followed by guards, appears in the doorway. "So she has deceived me and dies for love of him," he says bitterly, watching as Leonora falls to the ground. The guards spring upon Manrico and lead him forth to be executed. The Count has had no intention of keeping his word to Leonora.

Azucena awakes and, leaping to her feet, she calls for her son but sees only the Count di Luna watching her with malice in his eyes. "Here, look at that," he shouts and drags her to the barred window from which she may witness the execution of Manrico. "Stop them! Stop them!" she screams, hiding her face in her hands and swaying on her feet.

"He is dead," announces the Count who has been gazing steadily out of the window.

"Dead!" Azucena repeats the word after him. Then she screams, "Do you know what you have done? You have killed your own brother! I am the gypsy who stole him! O Mother! You are avenged!" Laughing wildly she falls dying to the ground.

The Count, completely shattered by what he has learned, leans upon his sword and stares fixedly before him. "The Troubadour . . . . my brother!" He can scarcely speak the words.

LOHENGRIN
or
THE SWAN KNIGHT
by RICHARD WAGNER

Lohengrin

SOFT and high, quivering with mystic light, sound the ethereal chords which usher in the prelude to this opera.

The music, so rarely beautiful, breathes romance, poetry and mystery out of which this tale of long ago unfolds.

One day, a thousand years ago, the people of Brabant had gathered to greet their well-loved sovereign, King Henry of Germany, known in history as King Henry the Fowler. He reigned from 912 to 936 and was celebrated far and near for his wise and kindly rule.

When the curtain rises King Henry is seated underneath the famed "Judgment Oak" where many treaties have been signed and bloody deeds avenged. Around him are his Saxon nobles who have traveled with him from the distant imperial court to greet his subjects here. Before him stand the nobles of Brabant headed by Frederick of Telramund. By the side of Telramund stands Ortrud, his wife, the proud dark-eyed daughter of a Friesland prince. The vassals are gathered behind the nobles in great numbers, and crowd down to the very banks of the River Scheldt which takes its winding course across the meadows to a city of tall gables and taller spires—Antwerp, the pride of all Brabant.

The King's face is stern and dark. Strange tales of civil strife, of scandalous accusations, of whispered treachery have come to him. The young Duke Godfrey, heir to the throne, has mysteriously disappeared. Some say that he is dead. Others suggest that the lovely Princess Elsa, elder sister of Godfrey, may be able to reveal his fate. Was she not with him the day he vanished? And if he were dead would she not reign in his place? These ugly thoughts have cast a gloom over all the land.

Now the King stands up to begin the "judgment". Four royal trumpeters sound a blast and call for silence. Henry greets his loyal subjects and then calls upon Frederick of Telramund, foremost of all the nobles of Brabant, to tell what he may know of this grave matter, saying, "I look upon you as a brave and loyal knight. Tell me what you know."

"Gracious Sovereign," Telramund replies, "I will speak the truth for falsehood I disdain." The people press closer so that they will not miss a word and he continues, "When death came to our valiant Duke he chose me as guardian of his children—Elsa, the maiden, and her young brother, Godfrey. Their welfare was with me a point of honor. Realize then my grief when, one day, Elsa returned alone from wandering in the woods with her brother, saying that she had lost him, she knew not how! When I questioned her, her pallor and her faltering words proclaimed her guilt!"

Indignant murmurs expressing doubt of his words run through the crowd but Telramund continues in a louder voice: "I now accuse this Elsa, Princess of Brabant, of her brother's murder! She being guilty I now claim the right to rule this realm as nearest kinsman to the Duke, her father. O King! Give judgment! You have heard all!"

"A dreadful accusation you have brought," declares the King with sadness. "Now summon the Princess," he commands, and, to himself, he says, "Heaven help me to judge aright."

Elsa appears walking slowly and almost timidly, followed by the ladies of her train. She is dressed in white and is so fair and young that the people murmur with sympathy as she moves forward to stand before the King.

"Are you Elsa of Brabant?" asks the King gently. He can scarcely find it in his heart to believe her guilty. "Are you willing to be judged by me?" As Elsa bows her head slowly he continues, "Do you know the dark charges brought against you?" Again Elsa bows her head but maintains silence which gives the King and the people a feeling of concern. When the Sovereign questions her further Elsa's only reply, spoken in a low voice, is, "My poor brother!"

"Elsa, confide in me," urges the King as though speaking to a grief-stricken child. "What is your defence?" During the long silence which follows the King and people watch her with keen suspense. Elsa stands motionless as though seeing a vision. At last she speaks.

"Often through sleepless nights I have prayed in my sorrow imploring heaven to aid me. At last, one night, peace came and with it blessed sleep . . . . I saw a noble knight in shining armor looking upon me with tranquil gaze. He spoke tenderly promising to help me . . . and then, even as I watched, he soared upward into clouds of light." Her face is transfigured with rapture as she recalls her dream and then cries out, "My protector, my defender, *you* shall be my champion!"

Elsa's Dream

All are moved by the strange power behind her words and the King implores Telramund to reconsider his accusation, but he coldly refuses, declaring, "I have proof of her guilt—a witness who saw the deed!" He then offers to fight anyone who doubts him.

The people shout, "Let God be the judge! Let Heaven send a sign!" The King asks Telramund if he will agree to fight any knight who may champion Elsa's cause. When Telramund signifies his assent, the King then turns to Elsa, saying, "Name the one who shall defend you."

"That noble knight of my dream shall be my champion!" announces the Princess, "and when Heaven sends him I will gladly give him these lands, my crown, and myself, if he wills it so."

"Send out the challenge," commands the King and the royal trumpeters send a resounding call to the north and then the south, east and west. After every summons the herald announces, "He who would battle here for Elsa of Brabant, let him appear!"

The deathlike silence which follows is broken by Telramund who sneers, "See now if I have spoken false or told the truth!"

Elsa makes piteous appeal to the King to have the summons sounded once again. "He may have far to come," she says naively and falls on her knees to pray while her women, following her example, mingle their prayers with hers.

From the vassals nearest the river now come exclamations of wonder. "A swan! A swan!" they shout as a tiny skiff drawn by a snow-white swan glides down the river. In the boat stands a knight in shining armor. The King marvels at this miracle and Elsa stands as though transfixed. Telramund looks on in speechless terror while his haughty wife, Ortrud, seems dismayed at sight of the swan.

As the strange knight reaches the shore the crowd, overcome with awe, is silent. The men have bared their heads and now break forth with cries of "A miracle! A miracle! A champion sent from Heaven!" The knight gravely returns their greeting and then, turning, says farewell to the graceful swan which has brought him safely to his goal.

Lohengrin's Farewell to the Swan

my faith - ful swan

With all eyes upon him the knight steps before the King and makes obeisance, saying, "Hail, gracious Sovereign."

"We welcome you, Sir Knight," returns the King. "Heaven has sent you in our hour of need."

"I come to defend a fair maiden who has been unjustly accused," the knight explains.

Then turning to Elsa he makes this request: "Grant me the boon, Elsa of Brabant, to fight as your champion this day. Will you entrust your cause to me?"

Elsa, who has been standing as though spellbound from the moment of her first glimpse of the knight of her dream replies, "My Protector! My Champion! I entrust myself to you!"

With sudden ardor the knight asks her to be his bride if he wins in the combat. When Elsa joyfully consents he says with profound meaning in his voice, "Elsa, if our lives are to be united, one solemn promise I must have from you. Never ask me who I am or whence I came!"

"I promise!" cries Elsa. "I take you at your word!"

"But do you truly understand?" repeats her champion, and once again Elsa gives her solemn promise never to question him. The knight then turns to the people and in a voice which all may hear he says, "Freemen of this noble land, Elsa of Brabant is guiltless. And you, Count Telramund, take heed—your charge is false!"

The Brabantian nobles urge Telramund to give up the combat. "What chance have you?" they ask him. "Heaven has sent this champion."

"Sooner than yield I will die with my sword in my hand," Telramund declares through clenched teeth. "If right is to prevail, I shall be the victor!"

At once six nobles measure with solemn strides the space set aside for the combat. King Henry strikes three blows with his sword upon his

shield as a signal to begin. The two combatants face each other and spring into action. They both thrust and parry skillfully as they go round and round with ever fiercer give and take. At length the unknown knight fells Elsa's accuser. Standing over Telramund the victor says, "I have you at my mercy but I will spare you. Go, and make your peace with God!"

"Victory! Victory! Heaven has spoken!" cry the vassals. In a tumult of joy they raise the champion on his shield while others place Elsa on the King's shield and bear them away in a triumphant procession.

The heart of Antwerp lies before us when the curtain rises for the next act. It is night and the busy city sleeps. Only the knights are awake and banqueting in hilarious mood behind the lighted windows of the palace which may be seen to one side of the stage. Opposite is the Kemmenate where the princesses and ladies of the court live. In the foreground steps lead to the massive portals of the great cathedral where at dawn Elsa and her Swan Knight are to be married.

In the dark two wretched creatures hold converse in low tones—Count Telramund, who has been disgraced and exiled, and Ortrud, his evil-hearted wife.

"What mysterious spell binds me to you, unholy woman?" demands Telramund. "Why do I not fly from you to find some peace for my distracted soul? It is you who have led me to shame!" And he cries out with anguish, "My sword lies stained and broken, my shield ground into the earth, my knighthood lost!"

"You consume your heart in idle grief," says Ortrud bitterly.

"I would I had a sword to strike you dead!" he mutters.

"You speak well," she says in mocking tones, "for one whose name means peace. Why do you mistrust me?"

"Mistrust you?" snarls Telramund. "Was it not you who led me to accuse the innocent? Did you not tell me that, watching from your castle tower, you saw Elsa drown her brother in the moat? And you lied!" shouts Telramund choking with rage. "Heaven sent her champion and God and the right were on his side!"

"God?" Ortrud's tone is a sneer.

"How dare you speak His holy name?" exclaims Telramund.

Ortrud merely laughs in mockery and says, "Give me the chance and I will prove to you how weak is this God who fights for him."

"Would you lead me to even lower depths of shame, you godless woman!" cries Telramund in desperation. Ortrud, seeking to quiet him, reminds him of the promise the strange knight has drawn from Elsa, the promise never to ask who he is or whence he came. She goes on to assure her despairing husband that, should this secret become known, the knight would be rendered powerless. She then reveals her plan to instil doubt in Elsa's soul so that she may be tempted to put the fatal questions to him.

"If this fails us," continues Ortrud, "we must use force. Where power is gained through magic art, the spell is shattered by the slightest wound. If you can shed but one drop of his blood he will be in your power!" Telramund's failing courage revives at these words, but he still doubts her sincerity.

"If you speak falsely now," he threatens, "woe to you." But haughty Ortrud only laughs in scorn and then quickly places her finger to her lip to silence him as the casement of Elsa's window opens and she steps out on the balcony. She is again clothed in the white of innocence and purity. Thinking herself alone, she sings softly to the night breezes of the happiness in her heart.

Ye wand'ring breezes

Ortrud now tells Telramund to leave her alone with Elsa, and when the latter finishes her song Ortrud calls to her. The words, "O Elsa!" sound strangely plaintive in the darkness. Ortrud makes herself known, manages to regain Elsa's confidence, and is invited to spend the night in the shelter of the Kemmenate. Between the time that Elsa leaves the balcony and her reappearance at the entrance below, Ortrud has time to reveal all the cruelty in her heart as well as her thirst for vengeance. Like a magnificent tragedy queen she calls upon her gods to aid her.

Odin! Thou strongest, mighty One!
Freya, O Queen! Bend down to me!
Prosper my cause with deadly guile,
Smile on my vengeance!

Elsa stands in the entrance holding a lighted taper and now calls gently to Ortrud who comes forward pretending abasement. With assumed reluctance she follows Elsa within. First, however, she disturbs her bene-factress by saying, "Do not count too much on your happiness. I warn you, as a friend. Perchance my gift for magic can protect you, should you ever need it. Let us hope that he who came to you so mysteriously will not leave you in the same strange way!" Thus she strives to sow the seeds of doubt and fear in Elsa's heart.

As the two women, so strikingly different, disappear within, Telramund, who is slinking near in the darkness, mutters, "Now dis-aster enters yonder door. You godless one," (meaning Ortrud) "I have no wish or power to stay your hand. Do your hateful work! But this I swear that you, who are the cause, shall share my ruin!"

The day dawns. It is Elsa's wedding-day. Trumpeters in the palace towers sound a merry reveille and from a distant tower comes an answer-ing call. Soon the palace gates swing open and the sleeping city wakes. Busy servitors hurry hither and yon about their various duties. As the day grows brighter important burghers of Antwerp gather in the square in front of the cathedral and are presently joined by nobles of the court.

The King's own herald now appears, preceded by four trumpeters, and, after a call for silence he announces the King's decree to the assembled crowd.

> Beneath a ban he lays Count Telramund
> For tempting Heaven with treacherous intent.
> Whoever harbors or befriends the man
> Shall share his punishment.

This decree meets with general approval. Then the herald speaks again:

> Now hear further what the King decrees:
> The hero sent to you by Heaven's will
> And who has won the Princess Elsa's heart,
> Is to receive both lands and crown,
> But does refuse to take the rank of Duke.
> Call him instead, the Guardian of Brabant.

They are then told that all are invited to the wedding feast and that at dawn of the next day the new Guardian of Brabant will be ready to lead them in defence of their country. The message is received by delighted cries of approval from all sides. The royal pages shout, "Make way! Make way! Our Princess Elsa comes!"

Elsa appears in her bridal dress followed by her attendants. At her appearance the crowd stand aside to form a passage through which the procession may pass to the cathedral doors. One of the last to appear is Ortrud proudly wearing a costly gown which Elsa has given her for the wedding. When the young Princess reaches the first step at the entrance to the church, Ortrud suddenly pushes herself through the throng, leaps up the steps and bars the way.

With blazing eyes she shouts to the astonished Princess, "I will no longer follow you in servile manner. My place is first, and you must follow me!"

"What is she saying?" the people exclaim.

"Ortrud, what does this mean?" Elsa cries. "Your tone is different from the supplicating one with which you came to me last night!"

"If for a day I forgot my rightful place," says Ortrud hotly, "think not I will remain longer at your feet. I demand my rightful rank before you all!"

"How your words deceived me!" Elsa replies in dismay. "How dare you say these things . . . . you, the wife of one whom God and man have exiled."

"My lord's renown was great throughout the land," cries Ortrud in fierce defence of Telramund. "His honor was unimpaired until this unjust decree was meted out to him. How different, he, from the knight to whom *you* have given your trust. Who knows who *he* is?" she demands with a sneer. "You cannot even call him by his name!"

"Ruthless woman," Elsa cries, "you have no right to slander him, my chosen lord!"

Ortrud is still holding her place on the cathedral steps when shouts to make way for the King are heard. He now appears and, walking by his side, is Elsa's knight whom the people greet with happy shouts of "Guardian of Brabant." The Princess turns to him with outstretched arms begging him almost hysterically to protect and shield her.

"What is this disturbance?" asks the King looking about, and the face of Elsa's knight grows stern when he sees Ortrud holding the place she has usurped.

"What is that woman doing here?" he asks.

"My lord, forgive me for disobeying you," says Elsa, "but she came to me with words of pleading and I took her in for the night. Now she taunts me with harsh and bitter words for my boundless trust in you."

"You fiend! Leave her alone," shouts the knight in sudden anger. "Your evil arts have no place here!" Ortrud cowers at the hero's words and manner, but is soon reassured by the unexpected appearance of

Telramund who springs to her side. Believing that his wife has told him the truth, he now proclaims in a loud voice that the mystic knight has won his victory by evil sorcery and that it is for this reason he will not reveal his name. All stand aghast at this accusation but their faith in their hero remains unshaken.

The knight quietly replies that no one, not even the King, has the right to question him. "There is only one who can compel me to speak —Elsa!" He expects the Princess to show her confidence at this declaration but instead she stands quite still, pale and trembling. The King, however, hastily assures the knight of his faith in him and the people echo his words with glad shouts.

In the tumult Telramund has gained Elsa's side and now whispers, "I shall be near this night. Give me a chance but to draw one drop of his blood and I swear he must then declare what he now hides from you!" Again doubt enters Elsa's heart though she turns with love and faith to her champion and the wedding procession, so rudely interrupted, proceeds in peace.

The next scene shows a room in the royal palace. It is evening. Pages enter with lighted torches and range themselves along the walls. From one side comes Elsa, surrounded by her women, and from the other side her knight enters, accompanied by the King and nobles of the court. The attendants and pages sing a song of welcome.

Here comes the bride

At last Elsa and her hero knight find themselves alone. In the darkened room they seat themselves near a great window through which the moon is shining, and for a short time they are blissfully happy. It is not long, however, before Elsa's thoughts turn toward the hidden mystery and she begins to wonder, almost in spite of herself, who he can be. Timidly she ventures to express her thought but the knight adroitly changes the subject and the danger is averted. But again and again she finds herself struggling to ask the forbidden questions, and ever the temptation grows stronger.

In spite of all that the knight can say Elsa begins to argue and to plead with him. Why can he not tell her all about himself? She tells him that he cannot fully trust or love her if he must maintain this mystery. She even charges that his very silence condemns him! The knight implores her to remember her promise, speaks to her quietly at first, then with more and more urgency as her own excitement grows. She gradually loses all control of herself and although he now warns her frantically to stop before it is too late, he can no longer prevent the words which pour from her lips.

"I must know!" she cries, urged on by a power beyond her control. "Your name! Tell me! Your name!"

"Oh, Elsa," cries the knight in a shattered voice.

"Where is your home? From whence did you come?" Scarcely have the words of the last fatal question left her lips when she utters a cry of fear. "Save yourself," she gasps in terror, handing him his sword which has been lying beside the couch. Armed, he whirls around upon a figure crouching in the dark ready to strike from behind. He wards off the blow and kills his assassin. It is Telramund.

There is a moment of deathlike silence. The knight now realizes that the end of his dream of earthly happiness has come. "Oh, Elsa, what have you done!" he moans as Elsa sinks fainting at his feet.

He carries her tenderly to the couch and summons men servants who enter and carry away the body of Telramund. He then calls Elsa's attendants and instructs them to dress their mistress in white for her appearance before the King the next day. "There I will tell her all she asks," he says with infinite sadness in his voice, as with slow steps he leaves the room.

When the curtain rises on the last act the scene is exactly the same as at the beginning of the opera. The King is seated underneath the Judgment Oak surrounded by his nobles, and the warriors are gathered in front awaiting the call of their new leader. It is a bright clear morning and everyone is in a highly expectant mood after the exciting events of the previous day. They are suddenly silenced by horrified surprise when four vassals of Telramund enter bearing a stretcher covered with a cloak which they place before the King. All immediately sense that this is Telramund, but even to the King's inquiry the vassals respectfully reply that the Guardian of Brabant will explain.

Then Elsa comes. She is pale and sad, not at all the radiant bride her subjects had hoped to see. At last the mystic knight appears and is hailed joyously by all. His face too is sad beyond all words as he enters silently and stands before the King. After a few moments he states that the proud task of leading the warriors of Brabant into battle cannot be his!

"What mystery is hidden in your words?" exclaims the King.

"Not as defender but as suppliant I am here," replies the knight indicating the bier which holds the body of his foe. He then relates how Telramund had tried to strike him down and how in his own defense he had killed the Brabantian noble, already exiled and disgraced. "Did I do right?" he asks. The King and the people reassure him.

Then he speaks again more slowly and sadly and all listen breathlessly to his words, sensing a message of dread portent. "Through evil beguiling, Elsa, my beloved wife, has failed to give me perfect faith— the faith upon which alone our happiness could be built. Her impatient heart has made her break the vow she made. She has asked my name and whence I came."

"How could she so forget herself?" the men ask one another, and the women sigh, "Oh, Elsa, what have you done?"

"Vainly I hoped she would remain true," the knight continues, "but evil tongues have filled her heart with fear. Now I am here to reveal to her and to all of you my name and lineage."

The people stir in helpless dismay at his words and tensely wait his revelation. The knight stands silent for a moment. His expression changes to one of exaltation and he appears to see a vision far away. Then he begins.

Introduction to the Narrative

In distant lands, ne'er trod by mortal man,
A mighty fortress rises—Monsalvat,
And in the midst a wondrous temple stands,
Which holds a shrine most glorious on this earth.
Within the shrine, a precious cup—the Grail!

Awe and wonder stir the people as the knight continues. He tells of the Knights of the Holy Grail and how they are sent forth on sacred quests to defend the innocent. On such a quest he had come to Elsa of Brabant. . . . . At these words she moves helplessly, expressing her anguish, but no one dares to speak. . . . . The knight adds that, when sent to render such service, the holy messenger may remain on earth and enjoy earthly happiness only on the condition that the one dearest to him shall have "perfect faith" and shall not ask the forbidden questions. At the end of a year all is then revealed and happiness on earth assured.

But Elsa could not wait! She has failed the test and thus, without delay, he must return to Monsalvat, and to his holy duties as a Knight of the Grail.

"It is from thence I came," he now announces with a note of spiritual exaltation in his voice. "Lohengrin is my name!"

Those who hear him stand motionless with amazement and reverence. Then from the river comes a cry, "The Swan! The Swan!" The skiff in which Lohengrin had so mysteriously arrived now glides down the river, drawn by the same swan.. Lohengrin goes to meet it and, as it touches shore, he says, "Too long I stay. I must obey the Grail." Then addressing the white messenger, he adds with sorrow, "My faithful swan, O would this summons had not come!"

Lohengrin turns then to Elsa and taking her in his arms he says, "If you had held to perfect faith in me, fair Elsa, you would have seen again in a year's time, your lost brother, Godfrey, whom the Grail has protected. If he returns when I am far away, give him this horn, this sword, this ring. The horn will bring him succor when in danger. The sword will help him conquer every foe. The ring will remind him of one who befriended him." Slowly Lohengrin parts from her and walks toward the skiff.

At these words, Ortrud, who is still vindictive and believes herself triumphant, leaps forward and cries out in a shrill voice, "See, Elsa! Your brother is leading your husband away! You will never see him again. It is I who, with my magic power, changed him into a swan!"

Ortrud has counted her triumph too soon. Lohengrin looks at her with pity, and then kneels in prayer. Soon a white dove flutters toward him and hovers over the skiff. Lohengrin, a look of ecstasy upon his face, rises and loosens the golden chain held in the beak of the swan. The bird sinks out of sight and in its place a handsome youth, Duke Godfrey, Elsa's brother, rises from the water. The Swan Knight assists him to the bank and turns to the people to say, "Behold, the ruler of Brabant!"

Ortrud shrieks and falls, her evil power forever broken. Godfrey finds himself in Elsa's arms and the people kneel in homage as much to the departing Lohengrin as to their young ruler.

With the golden chain in its beak, the dove gently guides the skiff down stream. As it follows the course of the river the knight in shining armor seems a figure of light as he stands bent upon his shield, deep in holy thought. Elsa's new-found joy is turned to bitter woe as she gazes with tear-filled eyes at the rapidly disappearing skiff which bears away forever the mystic knight who has been her champion and defender.

AÏDA

or

THE CAPTIVE PRINCESS
by GIUSEPPE VERDI

Aïda

MORE than two thousand years ago the capital of Egypt was a beautiful city called Memphis. It has long since fallen into ruin, but in those ancient days when Pharaoh was king, he reigned there in glory. The King of Egypt at that time had as many cares of state as any king or dictator or president today. The ancient Egyptians were often at war with the Ethiopians, a dark-skinned race to the south of them, who constantly tried to invade the regions of the Nile.

Through a trusty messenger King Pharaoh has received the alarming news that once again there is an uprising. He is all the more surprised by this news since in the last war these Ethiopians had been completely vanquished in a battle below the First Cataract. When the Egyptians returned from this engagement they brought rich treasures from the palaces and temples of the enemy. The victors also captured many prisoners including some dark-skinned maidens who are now serving as slaves about the palace. One of them is of such outstanding beauty that even the King has noticed her. He recalls her name now . . . . Aïda.

The King is determined this time to stamp out the foe completely— and to do this he must find the right leader. Pharaoh strokes his long black beard thoughtfully as he ponders the question, and then suddenly has an inspiration. A young warrior who has distinguished himself in minor engagements has exhibited extraordinary ability as a military strategist. His name is Radames. Why not appoint him commander of the Egyptian forces?

Before Pharaoh can come to any further conclusion he is interrupted by the entrance of his daughter, the Princess Amneris. She has come to complain to her father of the haughty demeanor of a new slave, Aïda, whom she wishes to dismiss from her service as soon as possible.

"My dear, she was a very special captive and that is why I have had her placed in your personal entourage," the King explains blandly. "She certainly is beautiful!"

"Beautiful?" Amneris curls her lip disdainfully. "With that dark skin? She is not even pretty!"

"All the better foil for you then, my fair daughter," Pharaoh says adroitly.

"I know I should not bother you with my petty troubles," Amneris admits. "You have grave affairs of state to worry you, my father."

"Yes," acknowledges the King, shaking his head. "Yes," and he tells the Princess of the danger of a new war.

"Who would lead our soldiers?" Amneris inquires and the King admits that he has thought of placing young Radames at the head of the Egyptian forces. His daughter's evident pride and joy when she hears this piece of news reveals to Pharaoh that she has a deep interest in the young warrior. It is therefore arranged between them that, in the event of victory, Radames will be rewarded by receiving the hand of the Princess in marriage. The King is doubly pleased that the youthful hero chosen for such high honor is also the one who has found favor in the eyes of his daughter, the Princess Amneris.

The King now summons his attendants and sends word to Ramphis, the High Priest, to appear before him. It will be necessary to arrange a ceremonial for the proper announcement of Radames's high appointment. In those days the people still worshipped pagan gods and goddesses. To impress the populace the High Priest can announce that Radames has been chosen through "a divine oracle" spoken by Isis, the favorite goddess of the Egyptians. When Ramphis appears before his King all the details of the impressive ceremony are quickly arranged and the High Priest departs to make the necessary preparations.

When the curtain rises on the first act of the opera the scene is the great hall in the royal palace at Memphis. On either side are colonnades of white marble between which are statues and flowering shrubs. Toward the back is a great iron gate through which may be seen the picturesque temples and towers of the ancient city, and beyond, the silent pyramids are static against a deep blue sky.

Ramphis, the High Priest who presides over the pagan temples, is standing in the great hall. He is clothed in rich vestments and draws himself up in a pompous manner when he informs the young warrior before him that a new war threatens.

"Has sacred Isis been consulted?" asks Radames. Ramphis assures him that the goddess has been consulted and that she has even opened her stony lips to utter "a divine oracle" in which she has designated who shall be placed in command of the Egyptian forces. Ramphis looks at the young warrior significantly when he tells him this but adds, "I must now hasten to the King to apprise him of the divine command."

Left alone Radames exclaims, "What if that happy warrior should be I!" He imagines the joy of returning a victor acclaimed by all Memphis. As he thinks of this he realizes that his greatest happiness would be to tell Aïda whom he loves that it was for her he battled and won!

Heavenly Aïda (Celeste Aïda)

Radames is awakened from his happy day-dreaming by the entrance of the Princess Amneris who has long sought to win him for herself. From his manner she has surmised that he is secretly in love with some-one. Amneris is determined to find out if this is true and to learn who her unknown rival may be. Having surprised the young warrior in this moment of exaltation she now says, half maliciously, "What noble pride glows in your face! How lucky the woman who can inspire such rapture."

"A dream of proud ambition fills my heart," explains Radames and he innocently tells the Princess of the "oracle". He does not know that Amneris is already aware of his appointment and goes on to wonder if he could possibly be the one destined for such honors.

"Have you found no other dream to fill your heart—one more sweet, more to be desired?" she asks.

"I?" counters Radames dismayed at the thought that he may have betrayed his love for the slave Aïda. Noting his hesitation the Princess is filled with jealousy. At this moment a plaintive melody is heard which announces the approach of Aïda.

THE PRIZE SONG
Aïda Theme

andante

Aïda enters slowly and very humbly. It is evident that she has been crying. After one quick glance at Radames she pretends indifference but Amneris, noting this and also that Radames appears self-conscious, surmises that it must be Aïda whom he loves. To test her slave the Princess speaks to her with feigned kindness and asks why she has been weeping. Aïda explains that she cannot bear the thought of another war against her people.

"Are you sure there is not a more personal reason for your tears?" asks Amneris in a tone of such malicious sweetness that Radames, aware of her insincerity, fears for his and Aïda's secret hopes. Aïda replies evasively and lowers her eyes to hide her true feelings. They part at the sound of martial music.

The King appears with all the court. He is followed by Ramphis, the priests, and many of his subjects. Amneris enters and proudly takes her place at the King's side while Aïda lingers in the background and Radames anxiously awaits the words of the oracle.

"For a great cause have I summoned you, faithful sons of Egypt," says the King addressing his people. "A messenger, newly arrived, brings us grave tidings." Then at the command of the King the messenger is brought in to tell of the new invasion by the Ethiopians.

"How dare they!" the people cry.

"An intrepid warrior leads them—Amonasro," continues the messenger.

"Their king!" they shout.

"My father!" groans Aïda softly so that no one can hear.

"Already Thebes is under arms," concludes the messenger.

"War! War!" come shouts from all sides.

"It must be war to the death," declares the King. "Sacred Isis has spoken to aid us. The divine oracle designates the greatest of all leaders —Radames!"

"Radames! Radames!" they shout with gladness.

"Our leader!" says Amneris excitedly to herself.

"I am fearful. I tremble," murmurs Aïda.

"Repair to the Temple of Vulcan," commands the King addressing Radames, "and don the sacred armor." The people show their rejoicing by a rousing chorus in the midst of which Amneris seizes the royal standard and presents it to Radames with the fervent words, "May laurels crown thy brow!" All present take up the refrain and follow Radames when he leaves for the temple.

May laurels crown thy brow (Ritorna vincitor)

Aïda has remained behind. Now she repeats in despair the words which have been shouted so joyously, "May laurels crown thy brow!" "How can my lips pronounce these impious words that wish him victory over my father!" But when she thinks of her love for Radames she finds herself torn between such conflicting emotions that she falls on her knees, praying to her gods to take pity on her.

Aïda's Prayer

Now we see the "Scene of Consecration" in the Temple of Vulcan. Supporting the lofty dome are long rows of columns between which are ranged the images of the pagan gods of the Egyptians. Sacred emblems surmount the magnificent altar in the center and the smoke of incense rises from golden tripods on either side.

Before the altar stands Ramphis, the High Priest, in a position of adoration. Behind him the priestesses perform a sacred dance to the solemn chanting of the priests.

Sacred Chant and Dance

Radames enters unarmed and approaches the altar. A silver veil is held above his head and he is then invested with the sacred armor to the accompaniment of the solemn music which is part of the ritual.

The passing months have been a time of weary waiting for Aïda, whereas the Princess Amneris has been busy with dreams of triumph. News travels very slowly in the country of the Nile but at last word comes to the King that Radames has been victorious. Preparations are made at once to welcome him in state in the city of Thebes which he has recaptured from the enemy. There the King, Amneris, and all the court will do him honor. There the announcement will be made that the hero will be rewarded with the hand of Pharaoh's daughter.

The young victor however is still unaware of this arrangement. He has hoped in his hour of triumph to apprise the King and all the world of his love for the slave, Aïda, and to demand that she be raised to his own social status so that he may marry her.

Aïda, still in ignorance of his fate, is torn between anxiety for Radames and horror at what defeat will mean for her father and her people. When she receives a summons to appear before her mistress, the Princess, she welcomes it eagerly since it may mean that definite news has come at last.

The scene shows the Princess reclining on her couch in the hands of her tiring-women while Moorish slaves stand behind her, waving tall fans of ostrich plumes. Amneris is in an ugly mood. She pettishly pushes away the tray of jewels offered for her adornment, throws down the mirror in her hand, and even refuses to smile at the comical antics of six little black slaves who dance for her amusement.

Dance of Young Moorish Slaves

Amneris sends for Aïda. She must know for a certainty whether or not Aïda is a rival for Radames's love and she resolves to force her slave into a confession. When Aïda finally enters and approaches her couch, the Princess rises and greets her with an extravagant show of concern.

"Hapless Aïda!" is her greeting. "Your people have succumbed in battle!" When Aïda shows her grief over this news Amneris goes on to play her role of sympathizing friend by saying, "Try to be happy here. I will do all I can to make your lot a contented one."

"How can I be happy far from my native land—here, where the fate of my father and brothers is unknown to me?" cries Aïda.

"I pity you deeply," Amneris declares, "yet no human sorrow is lasting. Time may bring the healing power of love!" Aïda's ill-concealed feelings reveal much to Amneris who is watching her narrowly. Now the Princess asks, "What new emotion disturbs my gentle friend?" As Aïda still refrains from replying the Princess pleads, "Tell me your secret hopes. Trust in me. Among the warriors who have fought against your country there may be one who has awakened your love."

"What do you mean?" Aïda demands.

"Even though the leader may have fallen . . . ." Amneris speaks the fateful words with deliberation, but before she can finish Aïda cries out, "The leader . . . . fallen? What are you saying? Oh wretched fate!"

"Radames has been killed in battle," Amneris lies, and Aïda's uncontrollable sobs reveal only too well the secret of her heart.

"Hah! Then you do love him!" Amneris shrieks, throwing off her pretence of friendliness. "I guessed as much! Now look at me—I lied to you! Radames is alive and well!"

Forgetting everything else, Aïda falls on her knees with a cry of joyful thanksgiving. "He lives! Oh, gods, I thank you!" Amneris watches her with jealous fury.

"Yes, you do love him," she cries, "but so do I. Behold in me your rival . . . . I, Pharaoh's daughter!"

"You, my rival?" exclaims Aïda. "But then, what if it is so . . . ." She hastily checks the words she would have spoken, secure in Radames's love and casts herself at the feet of the Princess. "Oh, forgive me," she begs. "Forget my words! I die of anguish!"

"Tremble, you vile bond-maid." The voice of Amneris is cruel and cutting. "You shall soon regret your confession of love. You are in my power. I hate you and you will feel my vengeance!" The sound of martial music holds her attention for a moment.

"Come, follow me," commands Amneris in a hard voice. "When he returns a victor I will share the royal throne while you lie prostrate in the dust. How can you hope to rival me?" With a gesture of disdain Amneris sweeps away, leaving Aïda to sob her heart out in bitter tears.

The next scene is one of great splendor, a broad avenue in the city of Thebes. A triumphal arch has been erected for the reception of the victorious army and the street is filled with a vast crowd cheering and waving palm branches. On one side is the King's throne surmounted by a purple canopy. Amidst jubilant cries the King enters followed by all the court. He leads the Princess by the hand and escorts her to the throne where she stands beside him, haughty and regal in her gorgeous royal raiment. Aïda crouches in the background trembling in misery and fear.

The chorus of welcome changes to a brisk military march as the victorious Egyptian troops begin to file in preceded by trumpeters.

Egyptian March

The chariots of war follow and then more soldiers bearing treasures and idols from the enemy's palaces and temples. Groups of dancing girls come to liven the scene and at last, as the cries of the crowd increase to a frenzy of joy, Radames appears. He is borne on the shoulders of his officers and is sheltered by a sky-blue canopy. Now he stands before the

King, bowing low, and is asked to approach the throne so that the Princess may place the wreath of victory upon his brow.

This done, the King addresses Radames in a tone of great kindness declaring, "Whatever boon you ask will be freely granted."

"Then, O King, let first the prisoners be brought into your presence," Radames requests. Heavily guarded and in chains the prisoners file in and as the last one appears, Aïda cries out, "My father!" and rushes to him.

"Her father!" the crowd murmurs astonished and Amneris mutters, "And in our power."

"You, a prisoner!" Aïda exclaims as she embraces her parent.

"Hush." He speaks in an undertone. "Do not betray me." But his bearing and demeanor excite curiosity.

"Draw near," commands the King. "Who, then, are you?"

"Her father," Amonasro replies looking toward Aïda. "I have fought for King and country. Be merciful, O Mighty Ruler. Spare these men!" He makes a sweeping gesture to embrace the other prisoners.

"No! No!" objects Ramphis, the High Priest and the other priests join him in his protest. "Destroy these savage hordes," they cry, but the people beg their king to show mercy. Radames and Aïda have exchanged glances and the hero, seeing the grief on his loved one's face, thinks he has never seen her look more beautiful. Amneris bites her lips as she watches them.

The hero reminds the King of his promise to grant a boon and, putting aside for a moment his personal plea for the right to marry Aïda, Radames asks first that the prisoners be set free. The King is willing enough to comply but again meets with strong opposition from Ramphis and his fellow priests. At last he compromises by freeing all the prisoners except Aïda's father. Then, before Radames can speak again, the King addresses him kindly, saying, "The country owes all to you. The hand of the Princess Amneris is to be your reward. With her you shall one day reign over Egypt!"

This proclamation is greeted with joyous shouts from the populace. But Radames and Aïda are both stunned by these words that so suddenly crush all their hopes and plans. Amneris quietly rejoices in her hour of triumph.

During the ensuing excitement Amonasro draws near his daughter. He imagines her to be weeping over her country's defeat and whispers, "Take heart! Our day of vengeance is close at hand!"

A beautiful picture is revealed when the curtain rises on the next act.

It is a moonlight night on the banks of the Nile. The pillars of a temple gleam white through the palm trees. At first the only sound to break the calmness of the night is the lapping of tiny waves against the shore; then a mystic chant is heard, intoned softly within the temple. A luxurious barge, gliding up the river, approaches the shore. Amneris descends from it. She is closely veiled and attended by her women. Ramphis, the High Priest, and a body of guards follow her. Amneris has come here to pray for a blessing on her approaching marriage with Radames. With slow steps they enter the temple.

Since the day of his triumphant return the young warrior has found no way to escape this hateful marriage which fate is forcing upon him. He knows that refusal will cost him his career. He still has a wild hope that some solution can be found and has begged Aïda to meet him at this romantic spot to discuss a plan which may bring them happiness.

Aïda now makes her way cautiously through the bushes. "He will soon be here," she sighs mournfully, for she has lost hope for the future. "What will he say to me? If this is our last farewell, then I will find peace and forgetfulness in the waters of this dark stream." She weeps and, overcome with longing for her native land, she sees again all the charm and beauty of her distant home. As she repeats, over and over again, "My native land, nevermore shall I behold it," there sounds a soft strain of plaintive music which reflects the longing in her heart.

My Native Land

Her dreamy mood is interrupted by Amonasro who has escaped from prison and has discovered Aïda's plan to meet Radames at this spot. The people at court know only that Amonasro is Aïda's father. They are unaware that he is the King of Ethiopia, which makes Aïda a princess in her own right.

Now, finding his daughter in this mood of homesick longing,

Amonasro plays upon her love for her native land and loyalty to her own people. He demands that she use her power over Radames to draw from him secret information regarding the movements of the Egyptian army.

"By doing this you can defeat your powerful rival," he urges. "Your country, your throne, will again be yours. You will be the happy bride of him you love and he can share your throne. Once again you will see our smiling valleys, our verdant forests, and our temples of gold!"

After some hesitation Aïda is finally carried away by his words and consents to betray her lover for the possible future which her father pictures. With a last admonition to his daughter not to weaken in her resolve, King Amonasro leaves.

Radames soon appears. At first Aïda accuses her lover of disloyalty to her. Radames meets Aïda's reproaches with fervent assurances of his undying love and tells her of his plan to have the union with the Princess Amneris postponed in view of the fact that warfare is to be renewed. He hopes to return again as victor and to be able to demand of the King the right to marry Aïda.

"You are counting without the revengeful spirit of Amneris," objects Aïda. "Her wrath will fall upon me and my father."

"I will defend you," Radames asserts.

"That might prove useless," Aïda replies, "but there is another way for us to escape."

"Name it!" Radames cries.

"To flee with me," Aïda declares.

"Flee? Desert my country?" Radames is aghast at the idea but Aïda pleads so hard for the happiness they will find together that at last she breaks his resistance and he agrees to give up country, loyalty, even honor, for love of her.

"What road shall we take where we may be safe from your soldiers?" asks Aïda remembering her promise to her father.

"We can go by way of the Gorge of Napata," replies Radames, "where we have decided to fall on the enemy. None of my men will be there until tomorrow."

"Aha! The Gorge of Napata! Then there will I post my soldiers!" says a voice.

"Someone has overheard us!" Radames exclaims.

"It is I. Aïda's father, King of Ethiopia," and Amonasro springs from the underbrush.

Radames is taken completely by surprise. "You? . . . . Amonasro?

the King? . . . . What are you telling me?" He realizes as he says these words that he must deceive Amonasro about the military secret he has unwittingly betrayed and he now frantically denies what he has said. "No! No! It is false!" he cries.

Aïda and Amonasro try to console him by describing the glory which will be his in Ethiopia, but Radames refuses to listen. In spite of all that can be said he sees himself a traitor.

At this moment the doors of the temple open and the High Priest appears just in time to hear Radames accuse himself. The guards are ordered to surround him as Amneris looks on from the temple steps and Aïda and her father flee in the darkness.

Radames draws his sword and hands it to Ramphis, saying with sadness in his voice, "Priest of Isis, I yield to thee."

A short and tragic scene follows. The stage shows a passageway in the King's palace which leads in one direction to the Hall of Justice, and in the other to the dungeon where Radames is being held to await final judgment. Crouching near the portal is Amneris, now desperate and heart-broken. She knows that Radames was not a deliberate traitor but that he revealed the movements of the troops merely because he contemplated flight—flight with her hated rival! In spite of this Amneris casts aside her pride in order to make one last effort to win Radames for herself. She orders the guards to bring the prisoner before her.

When Radames appears she promises him freedom if he will marry her. But he is deaf to all her arguments, declaring that life holds nothing for him now and that he is prepared to die. Helpless before his determination and his scorn, Amneris withdraws.

The priests who are to sit in judgment enter the passageway. The Princess covers her face with her hands as they file past her intoning a solemn dirge. Soon the voice of the High Priest is heard pronouncing the words of the accusation before the prisoner.

"Radames! Radames! Radames!" he calls. "You have betrayed your country to aid the foe. Defend yourself!" Amneris listens with a kind of wild terror but not a sound comes from the lips of the accused.

"O spare him! He is innocent!" she cries, but once again the deep voice of Ramphis cries out the charge and once again there is silence.

A third time the voice of Ramphis is heard. "Radames! Radames! Radames! You have broken faith with your country, your King, your honor. Defend yourself!" For a third time the only answer is a deathlike silence.

The judgment is then pronounced. Radames is condemned to be buried alive in the underground dungeon which, when sealed, will become his tomb. Returning, the priests again pass Amneris who cries out, cursing them for this cruel deed. They move on, heedless even of their princess. In monotonous repetition they chant, "He is a traitor. He must die!"

For the last act the stage is divided into two levels, the upper one showing the interior of the Temple of Vulcan with glittering altar and ivory pillars. Below is the subterranean dungeon where Radames is imprisoned. Two priests are in the act of closing the entrance by lowering a huge block of stone into the opening.

"The fatal stone is in its place," says Radames mournfully. "This is my tomb. I shall never again see the light of day . . . . never see Aïda. . . . . My love, where are you? . . . . May you never know my fate!" His soliloquy is interrupted by a slight sound. Radames peers into the darkness. There . . . . a ghost . . . . a human shape . . . . stands in the shadows, and in another moment Aïda is in his arms. She has made her way to his tomb undetected so that she may die with him.

Their meeting brings a few moments of happiness to the lovers which they express in the following tender melody.

To die, so pure and lovely (Morir! si pura e bella!)

Above in the temple Amneris kneels on the fatal stone. She is veiled in black and wrings her hands in helpless despair as she realizes that the man she loves is dying. "Peace . . . . peace . . . . peace everlasting," is her broken prayer.

The priests monotonously chant a dirge as the song of the lovers grows fainter and fainter. Their voices finally cease. One last lingering "peace" comes from the lips of Amneris, the doleful chant ends, and the curtain falls.

LA BOHÈME

or
THE FOUR MUSKETEERS
by GIACOMO PUCCINI

La Bohème

THIS opera swings into action with boisterous music, and the curtain goes up without preamble or delay as soon as the first incisive chords crash their way through the orchestra.

We see a large room on the top floor of an old studio building in Paris in 1840. The sloping ceiling shows it to be directly under the mansard roof, and the furnishings are few and shabby. On one side the slant of the ceiling touches a rickety bed and near the door at the back stands a cupboard as bare as Mother Hubbard's. In the middle of the room is a plain table which serves for worktable and dining table. A dilapidated bench, a ramshackle chair or two and a coat stand are the only other pieces of furniture.

There is relief from the depressing poverty of the room through the great window to the north which reveals a wide expanse of Paris roofs, now white with snow. Near this window a young man is seated painting at his easel. He has named his canvas the "Passage of the Red Sea" and hopes it will prove a masterpiece. He is wearing an artist's smock and a picturesque velvet tam o' shanter pulled down over one ear. He often stops his work to lay aside his brushes and blow on fingers that are stiff with cold. The small grate at one end of the studio is black and cheerless.

This artist, Marcel, now addresses another young man who is standing by the window looking out with an air of bored discouragement. "This Red Sea," Marcel declares, "feels about as cold as though it were running down my back. "I'm positively frozen."

"Well," observes the other, whose name is Rudolph, "I must confess I'm not working by the sweat of my brow just at this moment, either. We must have a fire somehow." At this remark Marcel picks up a chair as though to smash it into kindling wood, and it is easy to guess that other chairs have come to the same inglorious end.

Rudolph stops him, seized with a sudden inspiration. "Not the chair. We need that," he says. "But see—here's something we do not need. *No one needs it.* The manuscript of my great play. Let the flame of its inspiration warm us!"

"You are not going to read it to me, I hope," Marcel says in mock dismay.

"No! We will burn it. It is the world's loss!" Rudolph says this with a comic gesture of dramatic resignation.

"Noble soul," is Marcel's comment. They reduce the bulky manuscript to a pile of loose pages, some of which they throw into the fireplace and light. At once there is a bright blaze and they stand before it, gratefully rubbing their hands in the cheerful warmth.

Rudolph and Marcel occupy this attic studio with two other gifted young men—Schaunard who is a musician, and Colline who is a student of philosophy. They are all having a hard time of it and share these bare quarters in order to cut expenses to the bone. Though all are capable of really good work, they live largely by their wits. They invariably try to make the best of any situation and to accept what fate brings them with a great show of good humor. At heart they are serious about their work and devoted to each other, equally ready to share prosperity or failure. They are known among their friends as "The Four Musketeers," and they ironically call themselves Rudolph, the "great" poet; Marcel, the "great" painter; Schaunard, the "great" musician; and Colline, the "great" philosopher.

Marcel and Rudolph are still warming themselves by the fitful blaze in the little grate when the door is banged open violently and Colline stamps in.

"Br-r-r-r, but it's cold," he says, rubbing his hands. "A fire here? How does that happen?" He joins the others in front of the fire-place and they explain that they are burning Rudolph's manuscript. As they watch page after page disappear they have great fun at the expense of the "famous" author. They comment on the "brilliance" of his writing, the "color" of his phrases and the "fire" of his thought.

Just then a knock at the door interrupts them, and to their immense surprise two errand boys come in. One is loaded down with a sack of wood, the other carries a large hamper from which they quickly extract all kinds of food, bottles of wine, and a box of cigars. They are still exclaiming over this manna from heaven when Schaunard, the musician, appears and jauntily throws a pocketful of coins into the air. The others scramble about like street urchins to capture them and at the same time pour out a thousand questions.

"If you can keep quiet long enough I'll tell you," Schaunard manages to say and then explains that an English gentleman who wanted to get rid of his wife's parrot had engaged him to play the piano for hours at a stretch, offering him a good round sum if he would keep on playing until the bird died. Just why Schaunard's musical performance was expected to kill the parrot was not explained, but the deed was accomplished and here was the result.

The "great" musician's hungry companions are busily placing the meat, sausages and other viands on the table when he suddenly stops them with a pompous gesture. "This food," he says, "must be put away for a rainy day. This is Christmas Eve! Why should we dine at home when we have money in our pockets? The bright lights of the Café Momus beckon and the Latin Quarter is making merry? No! We, too, must celebrate!"

His friends readily agree to this plan, but in order to start off the evening properly, they first open a bottle of wine. Just as they are drinking a toast to the pile of coins on the table (for Schaunard has emptied his pockets), there is a knock and the voice of their landlord demanding admittance. These care-free young artists have not paid the rent—which is not unusual—and now they are caught with money in full view on the table. They feel that they can find a better use for their money than to pay for the tumble-down roof over their heads so they ignore the persistent knocking until suddenly Marcel has a brilliant idea.

He goes to the door, unlocks it, pretends to be greatly delighted to see the landlord and invites him in. He is a small rotund person named Benoit. His bulging eyes gleam when he sees the money and he humbly asks for the rent instead of insistently demanding it in his usual bullying way.

"Why, of course, I'm so glad you came, sir." Marcel's voice is suspiciously cordial. "It saves me the trouble of hunting you up." The others are inclined to think that Marcel has unexpectedly lost his mind, but a wink reassures them. Now they invite Benoit to have a glass of wine with them and they drink his health. Again and again they fill his glass until they get the little man quite befuddled and bragging of all sorts of escapades. They pretend to be vastly amused until he happens to mention that he is married. This is Marcel's cue. "Married?" he exclaims. "Then it is high time for you to be going home, sir." Benoit is having too good a time to leave, but they all set upon him at once.

"Those stories of yours . . . . really quite shocking," declares Rudolph.

"Out with him!" commands Colline.

"I was scandalized!" throws in Schaunard.

"We won't listen to another word," says Marcel. All of this time they are pushing and jostling the little man toward the door in spite of his sputtering attempts to get in a word. At last out he goes, helped along by a playful kick from Rudolph. As the door slams, Marcel says, almost out of breath, "That is the way, Gentlemen, that I pay the rent!"

Laughing heartily they gather up the money and all leave except Rudolph who tells them to go ahead. He explains that he has some writing to finish and that he will soon join them. Left alone, he has scarcely settled himself at the table with his work when he hears a timid knock.

"Who is there?" demands Rudolph somewhat gruffly, thinking it may be the landlord again. Instead a soft voice says, "Pray excuse me. My candle has gone out!"

Rudolph throws open the door to find a pretty girl with an extinguished candle and a key in her hand. She explains that she cannot see in the dark to unlock her door further down the hall and asks him if he will be good enough to light her candle for her.

"Do come in," Rudolph invites her.

"Oh, no! Thank you!" As she says these words she is seized with a sudden spell of dizziness. Rudolph grasps her by the arm and leads her to a chair.

"Are you ill?" he asks anxiously.

"Oh . . . . it is nothing," she replies.

"But you look so pale," cries Rudolph, and pours out a glass of wine. "Here, take this."

"I feel much better now," she says after sipping the wine. "If you will kindly give me a light I will go now."

"So soon?" Rudolph's voice shows that he would like to have her stay.

"Yes, I must go. . . . . Thank you. Good night," she says with cool politeness after he has lit her candle and escorted her to the door. He returns at once to his work but in a moment his visitor is back. "Oh, how stupid of me," she says. "The key to my room. Did I leave it here?"

"Come in from the doorway," says Rudolph. "Your candle is flickering in the draught." As he speaks, it goes out and he brings his own from the table to light it. When that blows out too, leaving the room in darkness, she gropes her way to the chair and sits down while Rudolph feels around on the floor for the key. He soon finds it and an exclamation escapes him, but he has made up his mind to keep his visitor until they are better acquainted so he denies that he has found the key and pretends to go on searching. His guest also gropes around until his hand clasps hers and he refuses to let it go.

"Let me go! Let me go!" she cries, rising to her feet.

"Why can't you stay? Why can't we be friends?" demands Rudolph. Now he holds both her hands in his. "See! Your tiny hands are frozen. Let me warm them into life. Let me tell you who I am, and what I do, and how I live." His visitor is interested in spite of herself, and listens while he tells her about himself and his ambitions. He says that he is a poet and that, although he lives in poverty, his dreams and fancies make him rich. "Now *you* have come," he adds, "and you are better than all my dreaming!"

Rudolph's Narrative

Rudolph ends by saying, "Now it is your turn. Tell me who you are." After hesitating a moment, she begins:

They call me Mimi!

Mimi explains that she earns her living by embroidering flowers . . . . that she loves her work but that the flowers make her dream of

lovely, unreal things. She confesses that she is lonely in her little room "above the white house-tops". . . . . "I have nothing more to tell you," she ends simply. "I am only a neighbor come to trouble you."

The voices of Rudolph's friends can be heard from the street below. Rudolph opens the window, letting in a flood of moonlight.

"What has happened, you lazy fellow?" shouts Schaunard.

"I still have three lines to write," fibs Rudolph. He then urges them to go on to the Café and promises that he will join them directly. Turning, he sees Mimi in the moonlight and is enchanted by her delicate beauty. He sees her soft skin and her slight, graceful figure. But what enchants him most of all are her tiny white hands. *"You* are my dream!" he cries. Suddenly enraptured, he takes her in his arms and kisses her. Mimi at first objects, then yields to his embraces and he persuades her to come with him and meet his friends.

The next scene shows the Latin Quarter of Paris celebrating Christmas Eve. Crashing chords resound as the curtain rises.

The stage is crowded with merrymakers, shouting and blowing on tin horns. Their noise mingles with the calls of street vendors who roll their small carts along, selling oranges, roasted chestnuts, flowers, or Christmas toys. Gayly decorated booths line the square where the crowd, filled with the Christmas spirit, is spending its money freely.

At one booth Schaunard is carefully selecting a tin horn, tooting on many of them before he finds one to his liking. In front of a tiny clothing shop stands Colline, putting on his shabby overcoat which he has just had mended. Marcel eyes some pretty girls who are tripping about, arm in arm, and laughingly asks if anyone will give him a penny for his heart. Rudolph appears with Mimi walking gayly at his side. He proudly buys her a little pink bonnet in which she looks bewitching. To one side is the entrance of the Café Momus, with tables set out on the sidewalk.

Rudolph and his friends make their way to the table reserved for them. They all like Mimi at once and make her feel one of them. They commence their supper in a hilarious mood, enjoying themselves so much that they pay little attention to those about them.

A most elaborately gowned young woman now makes her way haughtily to a prominent table, followed by a fussy over-dressed old gentleman. "It is Musetta," whispers one of the girls nearby. "Yes, it's Musetta," murmur some of the women. "Look at her. Isn't she elegant!"

The old gentleman trundling along behind the young lady grumbles, "I have to follow you about just like a servant. I won't stand it any longer."

Without paying any attention to him, Musetta carefully selects the table she wants and seats herself, although her elderly escort complains that it is too chilly outside. Musetta replies crossly, "Don't be a Blue Beard." Her roving eye soon takes in Marcel and his friends and she is much disconcerted that they appear not to notice her. She knows them all very well for she and Marcel were once devoted to each other, before they quarrelled and parted. Though she would not admit it for a moment, Musetta is eager to "make up" and now determines to attract Marcel's attention.

But Marcel has already seen her and is so upset that both Colline and Schaunard notice it. Turning, they discover Musetta, too, and are secretly amused at her manoeuvers. When the waiter approaches her table, she throws a plate on the floor in a fit of temper. As the man stoops to pick up the pieces her patient old escort, Alcindoro, protests.

"Do be quiet, Musetta," he begs. But his words are unheeded. She is rapidly losing her temper altogether, and gives sharp contradictory orders to the waiter which keep him running back and forth to the great amusement of all the other guests. Suddenly she rises and starts to sing, looking in Marcel's direction with a great show of coquetry.

Musetta's Waltz Song

With every verse Musetta grows more daring until everyone realizes that she is singing the song to Marcel. He tries to be indifferent and when he finds himself weakening he says to Colline and Schaunard, "Do hold me back. Don't let me go to her." During the song the old gentleman at Musetta's table has tried to pull her down in her chair, to make her stop singing. Colline and Schaunard have risen in their places to watch the fun and all eyes are centered on the lady and her tantrums.

Musetta now decides to rid herself of her aged admirer. She suddenly clutches one foot with her hand, crying, "Oh, how it hurts! How it hurts!"

"What's the matter, my dear?" asks Alcindoro.

"I can't bear it. Take it off!" she insists, holding out one dainty foot. As her escort bends down, somewhat awkwardly, to take off her slipper, Musetta says, "There's a shoemaker close by. See if he can fix it." Scolding audibly about the offending slipper, Alcindoro places it under his coat and disappears in the direction of the shoe shop.

"This is better than a show," observes Schaunard to Colline, amused at Musetta's tactics and full of sympathy for their friend. Now that the coast is clear, Marcel makes his way to Musetta and they are soon friends again. "This is the final tableau," remarks Colline to Schaunard, watching the two. Marcel finally brings Musetta to their table. She is now quite subdued and a little shamefaced as she limps over on her shoeless foot. As soon as they are seated the waiter presents the bill.

"The bill!" exclaim Rudolph, Colline and Schaunard together.

"What a bother!" says Schaunard.

"Who told him to bring that?" demands Colline.

"Let's see it," says Marcel. They then pretend to go through their pockets, but very little remains of the riches which Schaunard had divided among them.

Musetta, once more in their good graces since she has made up with Marcel, asks the waiter for the bill. She looks it over and gives it back to him, saying, "Just make out one bill for the two tables. The old gentleman who dined with me will pay it all."

A band comes blaring down the street, turns into the square, and then passes on. Most of the crowd fall in behind and add their shouting and whistle blowing to the music. Marcel and Colline hoist Musetta on their shoulders and march along with the crowd. Rudolph and Mimi follow, and Schaunard brings up the rear, tooting on his horn.

Soon after their departure Alcindoro comes hobbling back with a parcel under his arm only to find the square silent and deserted. He looks about him in surprise and is dismayed when the waiter politely hands him the supper bill for the entire party. This is too much for the old gentleman who is still making comical gestures of protest when the curtain goes down.

All the fun and laughter of that jolly Christmas Eve are forgotten by the time the story is resumed. The rising curtain shows one of the huge iron toll-gates on the outskirts of Paris at dawn of a bleak February morning. The ground is covered with snow and the trees that loom out of the mist are white with hoar frost. A group of custom-house officials are nodding around a lighted charcoal stove. At one side is the entrance to a tavern with a large painting for its sign-board. This picture is the "masterpiece" which Marcel called the "Passage of the Red Sea". By this time it has been re-named the "Port of Marseilles" and has been used to pay his board bill.

The music heard as the curtain rises vividly portrays this early morning scene.

Street cleaners wait behind the toll-gate, stamping their feet and blowing on their frost-bitten fingers. An officer comes out of the tavern yawning, rouses the group dozing by the fire, and slowly opens the great gate. Market women enter with huge baskets of chickens, eggs, and cheese, and pass on in various directions calling hurried greetings. Some go down the Boulevard St. Jacques, others down the Rue d'Enfer which leads to the Latin Quarter. Church bells ring for matins.

Mimi enters from the Rue d'Enfer and looks about anxiously. She is pale and thin and poorly dressed. In spite of the cold she wears only a small shawl about her shoulders. She is suddenly seized with a violent fit of coughing and has to lean against a tree until she recovers. Seeing the custom-house officer, she goes to him and asks, "Is there a tavern near here where a painter is working?"

"There it is," says the officer pointing to the "Port of Marseilles." Mimi now approaches a serving-maid who has just come out. "Please call the painter, Marcel, for me. I must see him. Tell him that Mimi is waiting for him."

"Mimi!" cries Marcel a few minutes later, running toward her with both hands outstretched.

"I hoped I'd find you here," says Mimi relieved.

"Yes, we have been here for a month. Musetta is giving singing lessons and I—I am decorating the house-front!" He points with a comical gesture to the sign-board.

"Where is Rudolph?" asks Mimi.

"Here with me," Marcel replies. "But it is cold out here. Come in."

"No, no, I cannot," objects Mimi.

"Why not? What has happened?" asks Marcel surprised. He had hoped that Mimi had come to see Rudolph to make up a recent quarrel.

"Oh, Marcel, you must help me," Mimi sobs. "Rudolph is insanely jealous. No matter what I say or do he does not seem to trust me. And now he has left me!"

"It is better for two who do not understand each other to part," says Marcel. "Musetta and I are happy because our love is based on laughter and song and music." During their talk Mimi's coughing has worried Marcel. Now, since she will not go inside, he hurries to call Rudolph. Mimi remains within ear-shot while Marcel tries to draw Rudolph out. He talks of Rudolph's unhappiness and learns that his friend has made up his mind to step out of Mimi's life because of his deep love for her and because he cannot give her the comforts she should have. He feels that she may be able to have a happier and more prosperous life without him.

Mimi has also resolved to leave Rudolph because she does not wish to be a burden to him. This mutual self-sacrifice has led to their misunderstanding. Mimi's uncontrollable sobs now reveal her presence and Rudolph is overjoyed that she has come to him. He rushes to her and a long and touching scene follows. In spite of their love, however, Mimi is determined to leave him.

While Rudolph and Mimi are trying to solve their problem, Musetta and Marcel have another of their frequent quarrels and Musetta runs out of the tavern, vowing that she will never see Marcel again. He dashes after her and their comical fury is a dramatic relief from the pathos of Rudolph's and Mimi's farewell.

The curtain, when it rises for the last act, shows the bare studio in which the action of the opera began. Marcel sits at his easel vainly striving to concentrate on his painting. Rudolph, at the table, is pretending to write. Neither one is really working. They are merely chatting.

Music Introducing Act IV

Rudolph is making up a story that he knows will interest Marcel.

"In a carriage?" asks Marcel.

"Yes, a carriage and pair," says Rudolph. "It was Musetta, looking very prosperous." He watches to see how his friend will take this.

"I'm glad. Very glad!" says Marcel pretending to laugh.

"You humbug!" thinks Rudolph. "I know you are longing for her."

Marcel, who suddenly starts to paint with great vigor, remarks, "Guess who I saw."

"Who, Musetta?" asks Rudolph.

"No, Mimi!" Marcel replies.

"You saw her? That's strange." Rudolph leans back in his chair.

"Yes, in a carriage, looking like a duchess," Marcel says glibly.

"Delighted! I'm glad to hear it." Rudolph pretends to be disinterested.

"You liar," thinks Marcel. "You know you are pining for her."

"Now let's get to work," says Rudolph with sudden resolution. "Bah! This pen is useless."

"This paint brush is impossible," declares Marcel flinging it away. He stares at his canvas and then, making sure that he is unobserved, he takes a bunch of ribbons from his pocket and kisses it. Almost at the same moment Rudolph opens the table drawer, takes out the little pink bonnet that he bought for Mimi that happy Christmas Eve and clasps it to his heart. They both fall into a reverie which Rudolph interrupts by asking suddenly, "What time is it?"

"Time for yesterday's dinner." Marcel tries to speak lightly.

"Schaunard hasn't come back," observes Rudolph, but as he speaks Schaunard and Colline come in. Schaunard is carrying four rolls and Colline has a paper bag.

"Here we are," they shout.

"Well, what?" ask Rudolph and Marcel together.

Schaunard carefully places the rolls at four places on the table. "Only bread," sniffs Marcel.

"And a herring, Gentlemen," announces Colline taking the fish out of the bag. "Our dinner is served!" They seat themselves at the table and pretend to have a fine meal.

"This is food the gods would covet," declares Marcel munching his roll.

"Now the champagne must go in the ice," announces Schaunard with a flourish, placing a bottle of water in Colline's old hat.

"Choose, my lord,—salmon or turbot?" says Rudolph to Marcel, offering him part of his roll.

Pouring out a glass of water Marcel ceremoniously hands it to Schaunard. "Thank you, I dare not. I am going to a ball tonight," says Schaunard.

Colline, after dining voraciously on his roll, declares he must be leaving. "The King awaits me!" he says. The others rise and mockingly bow before him. They drink to his health, passing the single water goblet from one to the other. Schaunard now suggests "something in the way of a dance". They line up for a quadrille and are still in the midst of their fun when Musetta throws open the door.

"Musetta!" they all cry as Marcel rushes toward her.

"It is Mimi—Mimi is with me," she says in a voice hoarse with anxiety. "She is ill!"

By this time Rudolph is already in the hall where he finds Mimi huddled on the top step. He gathers her in his arms and, with the help of Marcel, carries her into the room and lays her on the bed. "Quick! Some water!" he gasps.

Mimi opens her eyes, sips a little water from the glass which Musetta holds for her, and then says weakly, "Rudolph, I have come back. Let me stay."

"My darling Mimi! Of course! Forever!" he cries. He induces her to lie back against the pillows as Musetta draws the others aside and explains that she had found Mimi and thought her to be dying. Mimi had expressed only one wish—to see Rudolph once more.

"What is there to give her?" she asks. "Coffee or wine?"

"Nothing. The larder is empty," is Marcel's dejected reply.

"I feel so cold," Mimi moans. "I wish I had my muff." Rudolph chafes her tiny hands in his and tries to warm them. Mimi calls to Marcel in a weak voice. "Marcel, listen to me. Be kind to Musetta."

"Yes, yes," says Marcel in a choking voice, clasping Musetta's hand.

Drawing him away from the bedside Musetta hastily takes off her ear-rings and says, "Here, take these and sell them. Buy a tonic for her and get a doctor." As Marcel turns to go she runs after him. "Listen! Perhaps that will be her last request on earth. I'll go after the muff. I'll go with you."

"Musetta, how good you are," says Marcel feelingly.

Meanwhile Colline has taken up his overcoat with the intention of pawning it to provide necessities for Mimi. He holds up the coat and sings a touching farewell to "this garment, old and rusty . . . . a faded friend".

Colline's Farewell to the Coat

He and Schaunard go out quietly together, leaving Rudolph and Mimi alone. The two lovers speak of their early days together and of their happiness, but Mimi soon falls back on the pillows, exhausted. When Marcel and Musetta return, they open the door cautiously. "Is she asleep?" they whisper.

"Just resting," Rudolph replies.

"Who is it?" asks Mimi opening her eyes. Then she smiles as Musetta places the muff in her hands. "Oh, how warm and furry it is. I can sleep now."

Rudolph, reassured at seeing Mimi fall asleep, moves quietly from the bedside. Musetta is heating the medicine she has brought when Schaunard and Colline come back. The former tiptoes to the bed, then utters a low exclamation and motions to Marcel to join him. Colline places a few coins on the table near Musetta and asks, "How is she?"

"You see she is quiet," says Rudolph in a low voice, then he catches the expression on the faces of Schaunard and Marcel. "What is it! What is it!" he cries wildly, guessing the truth as he stumbles toward the bed and throws himself on the lifeless form of Mimi. Musetta falls sobbing on her knees while the others gather around in mute sympathy.

TRISTAN and ISOLDE
or
THE
FATAL LOVE POTION
by RICHARD WAGNER

Tristan and Isolde

ANCIENT Celtic legends tell of Tristan and Isolde in the days, nearly a thousand years ago, when Ireland was a kingdom. Frequent wars raged between the Irish and the people of neighboring kingdoms. In one of these conflicts Cornwall was conquered by the Irish King who then sent Morold, a brave knight, to levy tribute on the conquered. Tristan, a Cornish knight and nephew to King Mark, ruler of Cornwall, at once challenged Morold to single combat rather than to see his land unjustly taxed.

Tristan, who was the victor in this fight, then sent the head of his adversary back to Ireland as an expression of Cornwall's scorn. Old King Mark even dared to follow this rebuke by asking for the hand of Isolde, beautiful daughter of the Irish King. Against the desire of the Princess, his offer has now been accepted. Sir Tristan secretly loves Isolde but hides his love since she is pledged to wed King Mark, the aged ruler of Cornwall whom she has never seen. Sir Tristan, in honor bound to serve his sovereign, has been appointed to escort the Princess from Ireland to her future home. They are now on board a royal vessel which is already nearing the Cornish coast.

The opening scene reveals Isolde's pavilion on the ship. Since this is a vessel bearing a royal bride it is hung with rich tapestries, and the vivid colors form an effective background for her dark hair and her white skin. Isolde is unhappy. She is hurt that Sir Tristan seems to spurn her for she is secretly in love with him. She can even forgive him for the death of Sir Morold to whom she was once betrothed.

Isolde throws herself upon a couch and buries her face in the silken cushions as though to hide from her thoughts. Brangaene, her faithful companion, has drawn aside a curtain and is gazing out over the sea. The voice of a sailor floats down to them from the upper deck.

Sailor's Song

He sings of the winds which are filling the sails and speeding the ship "homeward". Isolde takes offence at the refrain of the song which concludes with the words:

> *My Irish maiden, where are you now?*
> *Is it your sighs that are filling the sails,*
> *O winsome, Irish maid?*

In her overwrought state of mind she imagines that they contain an insult to herself. She springs up and cries, "Who dares to taunt me?" Then she turns to Brangaene and asks, "Where are we now?"

"Bluish stripes stretch out over the water," Brangaene replies. "Our ship is sailing swiftly. We should reach the coast of Cornwall before night falls."

"Never!" Isolde cries wildly.

"What are you saying, my mistress?" Brangaene demands, alarmed at this strange outbreak. She hastens to Isolde who continues to speak with growing excitement.

"How faint-hearted I am! How unworthy of you, my ancestors. Awake in me once more my sleeping will-power! Let it shatter this ship and let all upon it be cast to the mercy of the waves!" Her companion, growing more and more alarmed, seeks to quiet the Princess.

"I had a foreboding of ill when we set out upon this voyage," she says. "Dear Lady, tell me what secret is making you so wretched. Confide in me!"

"Give me air! I am choking!" Isolde cries, and Brangaene hastily draws the center curtains apart to reveal the forward part of the upper deck and the steps leading up to it. A number of sailors are busy about their tasks. Sir Tristan stands apart from them with arms folded and gazes out over the water. His loyal follower, Kurvenal, is reclining at his feet.

Isolde, from below, stares at Tristan and then, laughing unnaturally, she says to Brangaene, "What do you think of him?"

"Whom do you mean?" Brangaene asks, although her gaze has followed Isolde's.

"That brave knight who has not even the courage to look at me," Isolde replies bitterly.

"You mean Sir Tristan, my lady?" Brangaene asks. "He is extolled by all as a hero without peer. His fame is spread far and wide!" Brangaene is surprised at the strange manner of the Princess for she does not know the secret longing in Isolde's heart. Tristan's apparent indifference has aroused the Princess until her love has almost turned to hatred. She does not know that he is consumed with a secret passion for her and that it is out of loyalty to his uncle and sovereign, King Mark, that he keeps aloof. He is in constant fear that a single glance may betray his feelings.

Isolde now tells Brangaene to convey to Tristan the message that the Princess wishes to speak with him.

"Shall I beg him to come to you?" Brangaene asks.

"Beg him? No!" Isolde cries. With an imperious gesture she adds, "Tell him that I order him to come to me. I, Isolde, do command it!"

Brangaene slowly mounts the steps to carry out the command of the Princess. Kurvenal, observing her approach, pulls Sir Tristan's long cloak to get his attention. "Look out, my lord. A message from the Princess." Tristan starts, but quickly regains his composure. Brangaene advances timidly and explains that Isolde would like to speak with him.

"Is your lady tired out by the long voyage?" Tristan asks. "Tell her that we will reach our destination before sundown."

"It is my lady's wish that you should go to her now," Brangaene insists.

"Tell her," Tristan replies, "that when we reach those distant shores where my sovereign awaits his promised bride, I will lead her into the royal presence." Brangaene grows more urgent, but Tristan continues to evade the summons, declaring that he cannot leave his post on deck. "I must pilot this ship in safety to King Mark," he insists.

"Why do you mock me, Sir Tristan?" Brangaene at last demands. "Have my words been so obscure? Then listen to my lady's own words. 'Go,' she said. 'Order him to come to me. I, Isolde, do command it!' "

At these arrogant words repeated by Brangaene, Kurvenal springs up. "Let me answer that, my lord," he cries.

"What would you reply?" Tristan demands, curtly.

Without further ado Kurvenal addresses Brangaene. "I would say that although Cornwall's crown and England's isle are offered to this Irish maid, the one who brings to the King his Irish bride is the hero-knight, Sir Tristan! He will not make her his own, even though that might be his desire. Remind her of that! I care nothing for your lady's displeasure!"

Brangaene hears these words with deep chagrin and turns to go back to Isolde. At the same time Tristan attempts to silence Kurvenal but he is now thoroughly aroused and calls after Brangaene in a loud voice, "Remember that Sir Morold came all the way from Ireland to levy a heavy tax on Cornwall. Our hero, Tristan, fought him rather than see his land unjustly taxed. Morold was slain and his head sent back to

Ireland. Thus was the tax well paid! All hail our brave Sir Tristan!"

All Hail Our Brave Sir Tristan

The other knights, attendants and sailors take up the refrain and join in the chorus. Brangaene is greatly perturbed by this outburst and hurries back to her mistress. She falls at Isolde's feet. "Such an insulting answer!" she says when she can regain her breath.

"What does he say?" Isolde demands. "Tell me without fear."

"He tried to evade me," Brangaene explains, "but when I came straight to the point he insisted that he serves you most worthily by keeping his place on deck thereby to pilot the ship in safety to its harbor. When I finally repeated the very words of your imperious command his churl, Kurvenal, dared to reply with insults!"

"Every word of *his* answer reached my ear," Isolde replies bitterly. "Now that you know that Isolde is despised, learn the reason for those insulting words. How easily I could return insult with insult! I could tell of a frail boat that floated to Ireland's shores. A wounded knight lay in it who begged for the help of my magic healing art. He said that his name was 'Tantris' but I recognized him as 'Tristan' when I found a notch in the keen blade of his sword into which fitted the splinter I found in Morold's head, that trophy sent home through spite and hate."

Brangaene shows her consternation at what Isolde reveals but does not interrupt the Princess who continues with growing bitterness.

"Straightway I determined to slay the knight to pay for Morold's death, but a look from his eyes softened me. I dropped the sword and nursed him back to health. When he departed I hoped I would forget him!"

"O wonderful," Brangaene cries. "Then Tristan was the guest I sometimes helped to nurse."

"He swore that he loved me," Isolde confesses, "but see—he returns boldly to claim my hand for his aged kinsman, King Mark. Do you suppose that with Morold living, that Cornish ruler would have dared to court an Irish Princess?" She buries her face in her hands for a moment, then cries out, "Oh, woe is me! I should have stabbed him when I had the chance. Now I face slavery as the bride of that aged man! Curses on Tristan's head! Death to him! Death for me, too!"

Brangaene embraces Isolde with impetuous tenderness and strives to calm her. "Isolde, dear mistress, come, sit here. Why all this ranting?" and she draws Isolde to the couch. "Sir Tristan gives you Cornwall's kingdom," she continues. "How could he do more? Thus this glorious knight also serves his kingly uncle. Think what a wondrous gift he bestows upon you—a queen's dower!"

While Brangaene speaks, Isolde stares vacantly before her. "You call him a 'glorious knight' " she says. "And I—I must remain near him, suffering the anguish of unrequited love!"

Brangaene, now for the first time aware of Isolde's secret, exclaims, "Lives there a man who could not love you? Such a one must be drawn into bondage." Creeping closer to Isolde she speaks confidingly. "Remember your mother's magic arts. How could you venture overseas without their precious aid?" Brangaene brings a small golden casket and opens it before Isolde. "Surely this casket holds a magic potion . . . ." but as she draws forth a tiny flask, Isolde pushes it away angrily.

"Not that one," she cries. "This one will serve me better!" and she seizes another small flask which she shows to Brangaene.

"The death potion!" Brangaene cries, recoiling with horror. She takes it from Isolde and puts it back in the casket. At this moment the sailors shout "Ho! Heave ho! Hey!" for the ship is nearing the end of the voyage. Isolde rises quickly. "Our voyage has been swift," she says. "Oh, woe is me!"

Kurvenal enters boisterously and calls, "Arise, ladies!" We approach our journey's end. Sir Tristan bids you make ready for the landing."

Isolde shudders at his words but quickly regains her dignity. Turning to Kurvenal she says, "Take my greeting to your lord and tell him that if he would escort me to the King, he must first appear before me and beg my forgiveness for his unseemly behavior." Kurvenal makes a gesture of defiance, but Isolde continues, "I will not set foot on land until he comes to beg my pardon!"

"Be assured that I will give him your message," Kurvenal replies. "We shall see what he will say."

Isolde hurries to Brangaene who has been standing somewhat to one side and embraces her crying "Farewell, Brangaene! Greet everyone for me! Take greetings to my father and my mother!"

"What do you mean?" Brangaene cries. "Where are you going that I am not to be with you?"

"I am remaining here," Isolde declares, suddenly hiding her excitement. "Did you not hear? I am awaiting Tristan. I trust you to aid me. You are to prepare the cup of peace—you know what to do!"

"What are you saying?" Brangaene asks, trying to conceal her growing anxiety.

"Here it is," Isolde says, again taking the death potion from the casket. "Pour this into yonder golden goblet."

"Can I believe my eyes?" Brangaene gasps, receiving the flask with trembling hands.

"Will you be loyal?" Isolde demands.

"This fatal drink—for whom?" Brangaene asks.

"For him who betrayed my faith in him," Isolde tells her.

"Tristan?" Brangaene cries. "Do not ask this of me. Have pity!"

"Have pity on you, faint-hearted one?" Isolde exclaims. "I need this antidote for deepest woe. Do not fail me now!" Brangaene is by this time scarcely able to control herself, but Isolde continues firmly: "Will you obey me?"

Kurvenal enters and announces, "Sir Tristan comes!" Brangaene, who has been kneeling before Isolde, rises hurriedly. She is terrified and confused. But Isolde assumes an air of proud composure as she stands waiting for the knight. "Tell your master I await him," she says to Kurvenal.

Tristan appears and pauses respectfully at the entrance. "Your demands, my lady?" he asks.

"You are not afraid to ask my demands, yet you have been afraid to come into my presence," Isolde tells him.

"Honor binds me," Tristan replies.

"Scant honor you have shown me," Isolde says bitterly.

"It is the custom for him who escorts a promised bride to keep his distance," Tristan says gravely.

"If so careful of 'custom'," Isolde replies with sarcasm in her voice, "can you not learn another custom—that of turning an enemy into a friend?"

"An enemy? Who is this foe?" Tristan demands.

"I am!" Isolde declares. "I have sworn to avenge Morold's death! Was he not my betrothed, a noble Irish knight? Once you were in my power and I spared your life. Now the time for vengeance has arrived!"

"Then take my sword," Tristan replies, handing her his weapon. "If you so loved this lord, do not spare me a second time."

"Put up your sword," Isolde commands, "and drink this potion that will end our strife!" She motions to Brangaene who fills the goblet with the contents of another flask which she has secretly taken from the casket. As she hands it to Isolde, the voices of sailors are heard singing, "Ho! Heave ho!"

Tristan looks earnestly into the eyes of the Princess and realizes that Isolde intends him to drink the death potion. He welcomes this way of escape from the anguish of the thought of Isolde wedded to another. He accepts the goblet and says with deep feeling, "This is oblivion's kindly draught. I drink it with rapture!"

As he drinks, Isolde suddenly wrests the goblet from him and cries, "Let me share it with you!" She drains the goblet and throws it away. Tristan now gazes at her with wonder. Isolde, on her part, finds that she cannot turn her eyes away from his. They stand motionless.

Love Theme

"Tristan!" Isolde finally murmurs with trembling lips.

"Isolde!" cries Tristan in a transport of joy as he clasps her in his arms. They remain thus, unaware of their surroundings until Brangaene interrupts them in great excitement.

"Quick! The mantle—the royal robe," she cries. She places about Isolde's shoulders a magnificent robe with a long train which several attendants arrange with great care. Isolde seems scarcely to notice what is happening.

Kurvenal calls gayly, "Hail, Sir Tristan! King Mark approaches in a bark. He comes with his men to welcome his bride."

"Where are we?" Tristan cries, bewildered. Isolde also appears dazed and asks Brangaene the meaning of the sailors' shouts.

"Isolde! Dear mistress! Compose yourself," urges Brangaene.

"Why am I alive?" Isolde asks her. "What was in that phial?"

"The love potion," Brangaene confesses. At these words Isolde falls
half fainting into Tristan's arms. He raises her gently and gives her his
hand to lead her from the ship. They proceed as though in a dream,
followed by their attendants. From above the sailors shout, "Hail to
King Mark!"

The second act shows the gardens surrounding King Mark's castle in
Cornwall. It is a summer night and a bright moon lends glamor to the
romantic scene. Brangaene is standing on a flight of broad steps which
lead to a balcony. A torch flares brightly at the foot. The night is still
except for the sound of distant hunting horns to which Brangaene is
listening intently.

Hunting Horns

Isolde comes out upon the balcony and calls to Brangaene. "Can
you still hear them?" she asks.

"They are not very far away," Brangaene replies. "I can hear the
horns clearly."

"You are deceived by the rustling of the leaves," Isolde tells her.

"And you are deceived by your own impatience," Brangaene retorts.

Isolde now pretends to listen but she soon says, "No sound of horns
could be as sweet as the murmur of yonder fountain. Only the stillness
of the night assails my ears and in the dark my lover waits to come
to me."

"Oh, heed my warning!" Brangaene pleads. "I tell you your lover
is being spied upon. Beware of Melot!"

"You mean Sir Melot?" Isolde asks. "How mistaken you are! He
is Tristan's trusted friend. When Tristan is not able to come to me, he
stays with Melot."

"I tell you that Melot is seeking to win the King's confidence at the
expense of Tristan," Brangaene declares. "He is already sowing seeds of
suspicion in the King's mind. This hunt, tonight, so hastily planned, is
but a ruse."

"You foolish one, the hunt was devised for Tristan's sake so that he
could come to me in safety. Hurry to extinguish the torch," Isolde

commands. "It is the sign for which he has long been waiting."

"You are reckless tonight," Brangaene cries. "I implore you not to give the signal." But Isolde does not heed her warning. She takes the torch herself and throws it to the ground where it sputters and dies out. Peering into the darkness she suddenly makes a gesture of delight, waves her scarf in welcome, and runs to meet Tristan.

He comes joyfully, embraces her, and leads her to a broad stone bench. There he tells her again and again how much he loves her. He tells her how impatient he is at the hours spent away from her, and that it has seemed an endless time tonight before the sign that he might come to her.

"I put out the torch myself tonight," Isolde says. "Brangaene's fears mean nothing to me. Love gives me courage!" They sing together of their happiness.

Oh Night of Rapture! (Nacht der Liebe)

A silence falls between them as the orchestra plays on, the music expressing all the joy they feel in each other. But Brangaene watches and waits on the balcony, unable to rid herself of dread foreboding. Suddenly she utters a piercing scream. At the same moment Kurvenal rushes in with drawn sword, shouting, "Save yourself, Sir Tristan!" as King Mark appears accompanied by Melot and other courtiers. They are in hunting costume. Brangaene flies down the steps. Tristan rises and attempts to shield Isolde.

"Tell me, my Sovereign, was not my accusation just?" Melot asks the King. "I staked my head upon it. I have served you faithfully to preserve your honor!"

"Are you so sure?" demands the aged King, shattered by what he has just learned. "It fills my heart with anguish to find Tristan a traitor. Why then should I be so sure of Melot's honor?" The King now turns directly to Tristan who stands before him with downcast eyes. "This blow, Tristan, to me?" he says. "Where now has truth fled if Tristan can betray? Where now is faith if you, my Tristan, can be faithless?" The aged King goes on to tell of the mighty deeds and unfaltering loyalty of his young kinsman in the past. He speaks with tenderness of Isolde, "the proud and peerless princess who has lighted my cheerless life. You brought her here. Why must we all suffer this anguish?"

Tristan raises his eyes to King Mark with a pitiful expression. "O Monarch! truly I cannot tell you." He then turns and kisses Isolde gently on the forehead and asks her if she will follow where he now must go. At this action Melot springs forward and draws his sword.

"You villain!" he cries. Tristan quickly draws his own sword to defend himself. Casting a scornful glance at Melot, he cries, "This was my friend who now has played me false!" He sets upon his opponent, but as the latter raises his sword, Tristan lowers his guard and permits Melot to strike him. He falls wounded into Kurvenal's arms and sinks to the ground. Isolde throws herself beside him.

Melot lunges forward to slay Tristan where he lies but King Mark holds him back by force.

When the curtain rises on the last act it shows a neglected garden below the ramparts of Tristan's castle on the sea-coast of Brittany. A stone parapet at the back forms a protective sea wall. The scene is desolate.

The knight lies stretched upon a couch under a great tree. He is still suffering from the grievous wound Melot has inflicted. Kurvenal is anxiously bending over him. A shepherd in the distance plays a sad refrain upon his pipes.

Shepherd's Tune

rall......dim

slower and softer

The tune comes to an end and the old shepherd comes along the sea wall and inquires of Kurvenal, "Is he still asleep?"

"If he did awake," Kurvenal replies sadly, "it would be but to pass away forever unless she, who alone can help us, arrives in time. Can you discover no sail upon the sea?"

"I will play a merry tune if I do," the shepherd replies, "but tell me, friend, why does our lord languish there?"

"That I cannot tell you," Kurvenal answers. "Go and watch the sea. If you discover a sail, play your merry tune quickly." The shepherd scans the horizon, shading his eyes with his hand. He then shakes his head and walks slowly away playing his mournful music.

Tristan opens his eyes. "That tune I know well. Why do I wake to it?" he asks in a faint voice. "Where am I?" Kurvenal has given a start of glad surprise.

"Tristan! My lord! Life at last," he cries. "O thanks be to heaven!"

"Kurvenal—you? Where—am I?" Tristan asks again.

"You are in the halls of your fathers," Kurvenal tells him. "You are safe in Brittany."

"What awoke me?" Tristan wants to know.

"A herdsman's ditty," Kurvenal explains. "He shepherds your flocks on yonder hills."

"How did I come here?" Tristan demands.

"Not on a horse, I assure you of that," Kurvenal replies. "I bore you on my own shoulders to the ship which brought you here. Now you are at home once more. Here the wounds from which you suffer will heal."

"Ah, do you believe that? I know it is not so," Tristan asserts wearily, half closing his eyes. His mind seems now to wander and he imagines that he is about to meet Isolde, only waiting for her to extinguish the torch on the terrace of King Mark's castle. His words grow fainter and fainter until he finally sinks back, exhausted.

Kurvenal has listened to him with great sadness but he now rouses himself and eagerly tells Tristan that he will soon see Isolde. At first the knight scarcely grasps what Kurvenal is saying. When he finally does understand he is transported with joy and struggles for words with which to express his happiness. He draws his faithful retainer to him.

"O Kurvenal, you are my truest friend!" he says. "How can I thank you? You served our sovereign as faithfully as did I. But when I was false to my noble kinsman, you were false with me to protect me! Now hurry! Look out upon the sea. Can you not behold Isolde's ship?" As Kurvenal hesitates uncertain whether he should leave Tristan in his excited state, the shepherd once more sounds his sad refrain.

"There is yet no ship in sight," Kurvenal explains dejectedly. Tristan's excitement gradually wanes. He murmurs a few unintelligible words and falls back. Kurvenal bends over him, not knowing what to do. When at last the wounded knight regains consciousness, his first words are, "The ship? Is it yet in sight?"

"The ship? Be sure it will come today," Kurvenal says to console him.

Again Tristan's mind wanders. "Behold! Isolde is on board," he cries as though seeing a vision. "She smiles. She holds a cup. See her gracious bearing and her gentleness. Away, Kurvenal! Hasten to the watch-tower. The ship! The ship! It must be coming now!" As Kurvenal again hesitates to leave his lord in his weak and helpless state, the shepherd plays a merry tune. At the welcome sound Kurvenal waits no longer but rushes in mad haste to the watch-tower.

"Hurrah!" he shouts. "The ship! It comes from the north!" Placing his hands to his mouth he calls, "Ahoy! Ahoy!" and for Tristan's benefit he shouts, "How bravely the ship sails!"

"The flag! Is there a flag?" Tristan asks eagerly.

"Yes, her flag is on the masthead," Kurvenal says. "It is Isolde's ship!"

"Did I not tell you," Tristan calls joyfully, raising himself on his couch in his excitement. "Can you see her?" he demands.

"She is there," Kurvenal shouts back "I can see her waving."

"O loveliest of women," Tristan says. Then he calls to Kurvenal. "Hurry! The ship must be landing. Run down to help her!" Kurvenal does as he is bidden while Tristan first tosses on his couch and then rises from it in a frenzy of excitement. He stands erect and tears the bandage from his wound. "See, although my blood flows, Isolde brings healing," he cries. He staggers forward as he hears Isolde calling, "Tristan, Tristan! My beloved!"

She hastens to him and is just in time to catch him in her arms as the strength of his sudden excitement leaves him. He is only able to murmur her name before he dies. She calls to him frantically but he does not answer and she sinks down, senseless, upon his body.

Kurvenal has come in close behind Isolde and now stands still, incapable of speech or motion as he gazes upon the lifeless form of his master. The sound of voices mingled with the clash of weapons now comes from below the ramparts. The shepherd hastily clambers over the sea wall and speaks to Kurvenal in an undertone.

"Kurvenal, listen! There is another ship!" Kurvenal rouses himself and turns to look over the parapet.

"Fiends and furies!" he cries. "They are all here. I can see Melot and Mark on the beach. . . . . Help me quickly. Guard the gates!" As he gives these commands the pilot of Isolde's ship runs to them.

"Mark and his men have set upon us," he shouts. "Defence is vain. We are overpowered!"

"Stand by and help us," Kurvenal retorts. "While there is life left to me, no foe shall enter here!"

Brangaene's voice can be heard from below calling, "Isolde, my lady!"

"Brangaene's voice!" Kurvenal exclaims. She approaches in haste and begs him to open the barricaded gates.

"Open, Kurvenal," she cries. "Where is Isolde?"

"What do you want here?" he demands roughly.

"You have come with our enemies, false one." He is interrupted by Melot who shouts "Stand back, you fool! Unbar the gates!"

"Hurrah for the day on which I confront you," Kurvenal cries savagely. As Melot opposes him, Kurvenal quickly cuts him down, shouting, "There, now! Die, wretch!"

"Kurvenal, you madman!" cries Brangaene. "Listen to me! You are mistaken!" But Kurvenal refuses to listen. He and his men set upon King Mark and his followers although the King cries out, "Hold, you frantic man. It is a wild mistake. Tristan, where are you?"

By this time Kurvenal and his men have been driven back from the gates. Kurvenal, mortally wounded, totters toward Tristan and falls beside his master. At the same time Brangaene hastens to her mistress and is overjoyed to find Isolde regaining consciousness.

With a last word of devotion to his master, Kurvenal dies. King Mark looks on sadly, sighing, "Death has come to both. You, my hero Tristan, truest of friends, must you again be a traitor to your King when he comes to give you proof of his love? Awake, you faithless, faithful friend!" He sinks down sobbing beside the body of Tristan.

"Isolde, listen to me, beloved mistress," Brangaene cries. In her arms Isolde has revived. "I bring you glad tidings. As soon as you fled on your way to Tristan I hastened to the King to tell him of your innocence and that I had substituted a love potion for the death potion you had ordered. He forgave all and followed you in another ship that he might give you up and leave you free to wed Tristan." But Isolde stares straight before her without speaking.

Now the aged King addresses her. "Isolde," he cries. "Think what joy was mine when I learned that my dear kinsman was free from fault. I followed in your track with flying sails to give you to our hero, but woe journeyed more swiftly than the happiness I planned for you!" During this recital Isolde has remained motionless as though unaware of her surroundings.

"Do you not hear, Isolde, my lady?" Brangaene asks her. "Try to believe the truth!" But Isolde is apparently unconscious of those around her. She looks only at Tristan. The orchestra softly intones the music of the love theme which, when it occurs here, is commonly designated as the "Love Death" (Liebestod) since it marks the end of the earthly love of Tristan and Isolde.

After a time Isolde speaks. "He is smiling, my friends," she says softly, as though beholding a vision. "Ever brighter grows the radiance as he is borne on high. Hearken, friends! Do I alone hear the rush of celestial breezes which seem to waft me on their airy billows? . . . .How they rise and gleam and glisten! Shall I breathe them? Shall I listen? They drown the panting whirlwind of the earth. . . . . Only the sound of heavenly harmonies envelopes me in highest bliss!"

With the last words Isolde sinks into Brangaene's arms and dies, her face transfigured with joy. The aged King, broken with grief, invokes a blessing on the dead. The curtain falls.

RIGOLETTO

or

THE COURT JESTER
by GIUSEPPE VERDI

Rigoletto

DURING the Middle Ages it was customary for kings and nobles to employ a professional jester or buffoon for the amusement of themselves and their guests. This privileged "fool" wore a costume patched with bright colors and a cap with bells. He usually carried a fantastic wand decorated with ribbons as gay as his dress. Moreover the jester was frequently a hunchback since the people of those days believed that it would bring them good luck to touch a person with this affliction.

To hold his place the "court fool" had to be ready with sharp answers when addressed and apt at devising novel entertainment. He must also have a quick wit and a nimble tongue. Moreover, he was generally the confidant of his master and knew all the intrigues of the court.

Rigoletto who has the title role of this opera is the court jester in the employ of the young Duke of Mantua. He has become the privileged favorite of the Duke but he is feared and hated by the courtiers who realize that many of the foolish, even cruel, acts of the young Duke are instigated by his "fool" who is also his boon companion.

The first act shows a brilliant ball in the ducal palace. Cavaliers and ladies in the elegant costumes of the sixteenth century are dancing or promenading up and down, occasionally passing from the ballroom to other spacious salons while pages and footmen in the livery of the ducal house are busy offering refreshment.

The Duke himself now joins the festive throng. He looks very distinguished in his court dress as he engages himself in conversation with one of his intimate friends, a courtier named Borsa. The Duke tells Borsa that he is enamored of a young maiden whom he saw on the street one day as she was returning from church. Since then he has seen her often, he confesses, and has even been admitted to the garden of her home on a somewhat obscure street. She has told him practically nothing of herself but appears to be living alone with an elderly duenna or chaperone. The Duke also admits that he has made her think him a young student without wealth or social position.

Borsa listens politely and then, glancing about at the gay company, remarks that "there are many fair women" among the Duke's guests.

The Duke smilingly agrees but says, "The loveliest of them all is Ceprano's wife." And he watches the lady with undisguised admiration.

"Sh-h! Her husband will hear you," warns Borsa.

"What if he does?" laughs the Duke and proceeds to sing a cynical song about the charms of "every new love".

Mid the fair throng (Questo o quello)

The Duke now singles out the Countess Ceprano, gallantly kisses her hand, and is leading her toward one of the other salons when her husband, the Count, enters the ballroom in search of her. He observes their receding figures and follows them, his irritation quite apparent.

"He seems to be in ill temper," observes Rigoletto to some of the courtiers who have also been watching.

"The Duke must have his diversions," Borsa remarks.

"Right you are," agrees Rigoletto, and with a shrug of the shoulders, the hunchback limps after his master.

Another courtier now enters and goes from one to another of his friends whispering something that makes them all laugh. He tells them that Rigoletto has often been seen of late making his way stealthily and under cover of the dark to a certain dwelling. They at once surmise that the buffoon, for all his deformity, must be having a clandestine love affair and, since they all detest him, they look forward to this opportunity to tease him.

The truth is that Rigoletto, apparently so cynical and worldly wise, is a different man at heart. He has kept the circumstances of his private life a deep secret from the Duke and his courtiers. No one knows that the hunchback who is the butt of so many cruel jokes has a daughter whom he adores. He has brought her up very strictly throughout her motherless childhood, and has had a duenna watch over and protect her. Rigoletto has had this woman in his employ for years and places the utmost confidence in her.

Whenever the Jester can get away from his duties at court, he goes to his home by devious routes to see his beloved Gilda. She is so charming and beautiful that Rigoletto is consumed with fear lest one of the hardened courtiers may discover her and make love to her. It is on one of these visits that Rigoletto has been followed; and now the courtiers think they have a good joke on him, not dreaming that Gilda is his daughter.

They are still chuckling among themselves over the "jester's escapade" when he re-enters the ballroom with the Duke, followed by the Count Ceprano.

"What a meddlesome fellow that Ceprano is," the Duke remarks testily to his confidant, "but his wife is an angel!"

"Why not carry her off, then?" suggests Rigoletto, knowing that his master revels in new adventures.

"You are forgetting the Count," warns the Duke.

"Can you not have him put in prison?" asks Rigoletto, laughing as if at a joke.

"Ah, no!" replies his master, enjoying the raillery.

"Then why not banish him?" is Rigoletto's suggestion.

"You fool! I dare not!" For once the Duke's voice is curt.

"Why not this then," remarks the jester, making a sign as though cutting his throat.

"You black-hearted villain!" exclaims Count Ceprano who has overheard Rigoletto's last remark and has also seen his ominous gesture.

"Is this the head you speak of?" asks the Duke amusedly, placing his hand on the Count's shoulder.

"Yes! Of what use is a head like that?" laughs Rigoletto maliciously. At this impudent remark the Count flushes with anger and draws his sword, but the Duke quiets him. After the Count withdraws, the Duke calls to Rigoletto and reprimands him sharply, saying, "You always carry your jokes too far! Some day the anger you arouse may light on your own head."

"Pooh! No one can hurt me!" boasts the jester. As he says these words the aged Count Monterone enters. Although Rigoletto does not dream of it, this man is destined shortly to hurl a malediction against him which will haunt him the rest of his life.

Count Monterone has come to express his disapproval of the Duke's gay balls which the fascinating Countess Ceprano, his daughter, has been attending against the wish of husband and father. He speaks scornfully and his attire emphasizes his attitude. His tall, dignified figure in a doublet of black velvet stands out against the resplendent costumes of the other courtiers who are dressed in rich brocades of every hue or gleaming white satin embroidered in silver or gold.

As Count Monterone addresses the Duke in righteous anger, Rigoletto steps forward and impudently dares to ridicule him. The Duke, furious at having the pleasures of the ball interrupted, orders the arrest of the elderly courtier, crying, "Enough of this!"

As Monterone is led away by the guards he turns a baleful glance upon the Duke and Rigoletto. "Wicked and cruel are you both," he shouts, "since you can deride the just anguish of a parent who sees his daughter misled. A father's curse be on you both!" He is led away and, for once, the nimble-tongued jester is silent. The father's malevolent curse sends a shudder of superstitious fear through him which he tries vainly to conceal. The Duke hastily leaves the ballroom followed by many of the courtiers. After some hesitation Rigoletto limps along too, shaking his head.

The next act shows a quiet street with a modest dwelling on one side and a garden surrounded by a high stone wall. Rigoletto, wrapped in a long black cloak, makes his way stealthily toward this house. As he obviously wishes to remain unobserved, he is somewhat annoyed when a tall man who has been following him now approaches his side and speaks to him.

"Go along, I have nothing to give you," Rigoletto says abruptly.

"No matter, kind sir," replies the man respectfully. "I only wished to say that I have here a dagger which I know how to use . . . ."

"A robber?" asks Rigoletto.

"No. But a man who for a trifle would rid you of a rival," explains the stranger. Rigoletto hesitates a moment as though struck by a thought, then he asks, "What would it cost me to get rid of a nobleman?"

"More than for a man of lesser importance," replies the man. Rigoletto questions him further and learns that this professional assassin performs these little "acts of convenience" for one-half the stipulated fee in advance, and the balance when the deed is done. "Can I serve you?" he persists.

"Not now," replies Rigoletto. "What is your name?"

"Sparafucile," is the reply.

"Where can you be found?" asks the jester.

"I am hereabouts almost every night," answers Sparafucile.

"Very well then. Now go!" commands Rigoletto. Drawing his cloak closer about him he muses on this strange meeting. "How unlike we are," he says to himself. "My tongue is my weapon, the dagger, his! To make others laugh is my vocation while he makes people weep. . . . . How that old man cursed me!" He shakes the thought from him and continues to muse upon his own life. "It is hideous to be deformed and yet to play the clown. . . . . Tears, the solace of mankind are denied me! When a young and high-born master says, 'Amuse me, Clown!' I must obey! . . . . But that old man who cursed me . . . . O, why do his words haunt me so?"

Rigoletto reaches the garden gate and is greeted joyfully by his daughter.

Gilda's Meeting with her Father

Gilda, finding her father depressed, now says to him, "Why do you look so care-worn, dear Father? What troubles you?" Rigoletto tries to put her off, but she continues her questioning. She has only very recently come to know her father for she has been separated from him during her childhood. Only three months ago she was brought to Mantua with Giovanna, her duenna, and installed in this house. Gilda cannot understand why Rigoletto is so mysterious about his own movements, and why he seems determined that no one shall see her.

"What do you really do?" demands Gilda, but Rigoletto replies, "What does that matter to you?" He is unwilling to have his daughter know that he is the famous court jester for she will then also know that his fame is more ill than good. To change the subject he asks sternly, "Do you obey me? You never leave the house?"

"Only when I go to church," his daughter replies.

"That is right, my dear," he answers, relieved to find that his orders are being carried out.

"Have we no family, no friends?" asks Gilda with natural curiosity.

"None! You are 'family' and 'friends' and the whole universe to me!" her father replies with deep affection in his voice.

"Dear father, I wish I could be with you more," pleads Gilda. "It is now three months since I arrived here and as yet I have seen nothing of the city. With your permission I would like to go out more."

"Never! Never!" exclaims Rigoletto, anxiety in his voice. "I have told you never to leave the house alone. I must be obeyed!"

"I know," sighs Gilda resignedly, but to herself she murmurs, "Oh, what have I said!"

Rigoletto questions Giovanna who convinces him that no one is ever admitted to the house. He asks about the various gates to the garden and is solemnly assured that they are always locked. Just then there are sounds of footsteps which Rigoletto hastens to investigate. The Duke in the disguise of a "poor" young man is outside. When Rigoletto swings open the gate, the Duke leaps behind it and then quickly enters the garden and conceals himself behind some bushes, unseen by Gilda or her father. The latter comes back and, after once more warning his daughter about admitting strangers, takes his leave.

The Duke, overhearing their conversation in his hiding place, is astounded to learn that this is Rigoletto's home and that the lovely Gilda is the daughter of his court fool. This fact, however, only serves to add new zest to his adventure. For some time he has found it very easy to arrange meetings with Gilda for he has been able to silence Giovanna with large bribes and even to win her assistance. She has seen him now in the garden, and moves toward him so that he can press money into her hand.

"Giovanna, my conscience troubles me," says Gilda, still unaware that the Duke is in the garden.

"What about, pray?" asks Giovanna.

"I did not tell my father about that young man who comes here often . . . ."

"But why should you?" interrupts her companion. "He would put a stop to it. Would you like that?"

"Oh no!" cries Gilda. "I . . . . I like him!"

"He looks like a wealthy cavalier to me," observes Giovanna who has good reason to know.

"I do not care for position or wealth," exclaims simple-hearted Gilda. "The poorer he is, the better I would like it. How I long to say to him, 'I love . . . .' "

"I love you!" exclaims the Duke, taking the words out of her mouth. Gilda is overjoyed at seeing him and Giovanna discreetly withdraws to leave the lovers together. Taking advantage of this opportunity and Gilda's confession that she loves him, the Duke expresses his feeling for her in the following song.

Love is the Sun (E il sol dell' anima)

The Count has never told Gilda who he really is and, when she now asks him his name, he hesitates. Finally he says, "It is but a humble name—Walter Malde. I am a scholar and without wealth or position." This statement only endears him all the more to his gentle companion. But at this point their happy talk is interrupted by Giovanna who warns them of approaching footsteps.

"It may be my father!" gasps Gilda in terror. "Quick! Let him out by way of the terrace," she tells Giovanna. After a somewhat hasty farewell in which they pledge each other their undying love, the Duke leaves.

Count Ceprano and Borsa, one of the gentlemen of the court, have been responsible for the disturbing footsteps. "This is the place, I am sure," Borsa whispers to his companion as they pause near the garden gate and then hurry on their way. In order to settle his score with Rigoletto, Count Ceprano has persuaded a group of the courtiers to assist him in abducting the young girl from this house. They intend to play an unkind joke on the court jester, but they do not dream that the girl is Rigoletto's daughter. They plan to carry out their plot this very night.

Gilda, alone in the garden, dreams of her love and repeats, over and over again, the name which the Duke has given her as his own, until she feels it "carved" in her heart.

Carved within my inmost heart (Caro Nome)

By this time it has grown dark. Gilda slowly enters the house but soon appears on the terrace with a taper in her hand, still humming the refrain of her song. While she stands there, lovely in the flickering light, the dark street below is gradually filled with a group of courtiers, all masked and armed. Among them are Borsa, Marullo, and Count Ceprano. Rigoletto who has chosen this very time to return to his house stumbles against Borsa in the darkness.

"Who is there?" he inquires, but receives no reply as Borsa slips out of his way and warns his companions. "Keep quiet. It is Rigoletto."

" A double triumph, then," declares Count Ceprano. "This night shall be his last."

"No, no!" objects Borsa, "let him linger on for our diversion."

"Everybody ready?" asks Marullo.

"Who speaks?" demands Rigoletto who has been feeling his way along the stone wall.

"Is it you, Rigoletto?" asks Marullo, realizing that he is bound to discover them.

"Who is that?" Rigoletto asks in alarm, thinking only of his daughter.

"You will not betray us. I am Marullo."

"You are not here in the dead of night for any good," Rigoletto accuses him.

"No, but it is just a silly prank. We are going to abduct the Countess Ceprano," Marullo explains glibly.

"I breathe again," murmurs Rigoletto to himself. "But how will you get in?" he asks. Marullo motions to the Count to give him his key which he, in turn, hands to Rigoletto. "With this," he says.

Rigoletto fingers the key and, feeling the Count's crest upon it, begins to believe them. "The Count's palace is yonder. I will go with you," he offers.

"First put on this mask," commands Marullo.

"But why?" remonstrates Rigoletto. "The darkness hides us." Marullo, however, manages to put the mask on Rigoletto, and to hold it on, binds his eyes with a handkerchief. The jester is then asked to hold the foot of the ladder by which they pretend they are to scale the wall to Ceprano's palace.

Meanwhile the others silently break into Rigoletto's garden, invade Gilda's room, and return carrying Gilda who is gagged so that she can make no outcry. On the street she drops a scarf as they carry her swiftly away.

Rigoletto has been patiently holding the ladder for some time when the silence around him grows alarming. "Have you done it? This jest grows tedious!" he cries at last. Getting no reply, he tears off the bandage and the mask and realizes that he has been duped. By the light of a lantern which one of the conspirators has left, he spies Gilda's scarf which he recognizes at once. Then, horrified, he sees the open gate. Overcome with fear, he dashes madly into the house. When he comes out again, dragging the stupefied Giovanna after him, he at first stands speechless with horror and bewilderment. Finally he cries out in anguish, "Hah! A father cursed me!"

The next scene shows a richly furnished room in the ducal palace. The Duke enters. He appears disturbed for he has discovered that Gilda is missing. When he went to Rigoletto's home earlier in the day he found the doors open and the house deserted. Faced with the thought of losing Gilda he now suddenly feels that she is the only one he has ever really loved.

His courtiers do not find him in any mood to listen to their latest adventure but they do not hesitate to relate with great glee their escapade of the night before. The Duke listens indifferently at first, but when he hears them say that it was Rigoletto's house which they invaded, he realizes that it is they who have carried off Gilda. He is at once concerned to find out where she is.

"What has become of the lady?" he asks casually. "Where have you left her?"

"We did not 'leave' her anywhere," they tell him. "We brought her here to the palace." Upon learning this the Duke becomes preoccupied with thoughts of Gilda, and, forgetting them entirely, reveals his secret yearning for her in the following song.

Now Hope Renewed (Possente amor)

After the Duke has hastily left the room, Rigoletto's voice can be heard behind the scenes. "Poor Rigoletto," murmurs Marullo. He is probably the only one among the courtiers who feels any pity for the hunchback who now appears, assuming a jocular air to hide his anxiety.

"Good morning, Rigoletto," they greet him.

"They were all in the plot," Rigoletto says to himself .

"What is the good word this morning, buffoon?" asks Ceprano sneering.

"What is the good word this morning," repeats Rigoletto, imitating his voice and manner. "Only that you bore me more than usual!" They all attempt to laugh at this sally, but the situation is somewhat strained.

Torn with anxiety for his daughter, but not daring to accuse his tormentors directly, Rigoletto now says sarcastically, "I am happy to see that none of you took cold after being out so late last night!"

"Last night, did you say?" It is Marullo who speaks. "I never slept better!"

"Then I must have been dreaming," rejoins Rigoletto with bitterness. He turns to go, but stoops to pick up a handkerchief from the floor and examines it closely. "Not her's," he says under his breath while the courtiers watch him, highly amused. "Is the Duke still sleeping?" he asks.

"Yes," someone replies just as a page enters with a message for the Duke. "Is he not here?" the page inquires.

"He is still asleep," Count Ceprano tells him.

"But I saw his lordship just a few minutes ago," answers the page, surprised.

"He has gone hunting," Borsa throws in.

"Without his attendants?" the page exclaims, not understanding the gestures they are making to keep him quiet. Finally one of the courtiers goes to him and says through clenched teeth, "Can't you understand? The Duke is not to be disturbed!"

Rigoletto, who has been taking all this in, now rushes between them and cries out, "She is here, then! She is with the Duke!"

"Who?" they ask, pretending not to understand.

"The maiden whom you forcibly dragged from my house last night!" he shouts.

"You must be mad," they say, and their jeering tone drives him to a frenzy.

"No, I am sure she is here!" he cries, despair seizing him. "I must have her back—my daughter!"

"His daughter!" They look at each other in amazement. This puts a different face on the matter.

"Yes! My daughter! Give her back to me!" He struggles to get to the door leading to the Duke's private apartments, but is held back by the courtiers. Almost screaming in his wild rage he cries, "You minions! You parasites! You thieves! Have you sold her for a price? Your sordid souls are fit for any crime!" Again he struggles with them but at last falls back exhausted. Breaking into uncontrolled sobs, he now pleads with them to have pity. "It will cost you nothing to restore her to me, and she is all the world to me."

At this moment Gilda comes through the doorway her father has sought to enter and rushes, sobbing, into his arms. Rigoletto imperiously motions to the courtiers to withdraw and turns to comfort his daughter. She tells him of the abduction, her terror, the strange and beautiful room where she has been held a prisoner all night. She adds that the Duke had come to her there—he whom she supposed to be a person of humble circumstances and whom she had learned to love. Now she knows he has deceived her!

"We must go away from here, from the Court, within the hour," announces Rigoletto. "How completely our lives have changed," he says, and his daughter tearfully agrees.

Some time now elapses before the last act of this opera. Rigoletto has determined that the Duke shall pay with his life for the unhappiness he has brought upon Gilda. She, however, still loves the Duke although she considers herself disgraced by his perfidy. Her father intends to cure her of this infatuation by showing her that her ideal is not worthy of her love. He has therefore arranged with Sparafucile—who will do anything for a price—to lure the Duke to the murderer's lonely tavern. Here, on the same night, Rigoletto will also bring his love-sick daughter.

When the curtain rises on the last act, the scene shows a remote spot on the shores of the Muncio River. The tavern in the foreground, to one side, is a dilapidated two-story building. A path to the river runs along the stone wall of a garden. It is night, and in the distance can be seen the illumined towers of Mantua.

Rigoletto and Gilda stand huddled together outside the tavern. They are talking in low tones.

"You love him still?" Rigoletto is saying, bitterly.

"I cannot help it," Gilda admits in a tremulous voice.

"It is a mad infatuation," retorts Rigoletto hotly. "How weak is a woman's heart! Even if you would forgive him, I will not, my Gilda!"

"Have pity on him, father," she begs.

"If I prove his unfaithfulness will you then try to forget him?" asks her father, drawing her closer to one of the windows through which Sparafucile can be seen, cleaning his belt.

"I do not see him," says Gilda, almost hopefully.

"Wait a little," warns Rigoletto. Before long the Duke does appear, much to Gilda's dismay. He is dressed as a private soldier to hide his rank, and now orders a bottle of wine and attempts to make overtures to Sparafucile's pretty sister, Maddelene, who waits upon him. After a drink or two, the Duke sings a gay song about the fickleness of women.

Women are fickle (La donna è mobile)

Sparafucile comes out and draws Rigoletto to one side whispering, "Your man is here. Is he to live or die?"

"Wait near at hand for a while. I will let you know later," Rigoletto replies.

Gilda is amazed at the Duke's frivolity and is finally convinced of his falseness when she hears him address Maddelene with the same words of love he once spoke to her. She now voices her grief while her father swears vengeance. The Duke continues to make love to Maddelene, who tells him she "prizes" his "jokes" highly. The voices of Gilda and Rigoletto outside, and those of the Duke and Maddelene inside the tavern can all be heard at the same time.

The Quartet (Introduction)

The Quartet (Second Part)

[CONTINUED ON NEXT PAGE]

Gilda's father now tells her to return to their home at once, disguise herself as a youth, engage a horse, take whatever money she can find in the house, and ride to Verona. He promises to join her there the next day. Gilda begs her father to come with her and, when he refuses, she leaves with great reluctance. Rigoletto goes behind the tavern where he has a conference with Sparafucile. As they return he says, "Twenty crown pieces? Here are ten. When the deed is done, you shall have ten more. Is he still here?"

"Yes," replies Sparafucile.

"Carry out my orders. I will return at midnight," Rigoletto says with determination.

A storm is threatening which makes it easy for Sparafucile to persuade his intended victim to stay the night. Maddelene, however, has taken a fancy to the "pleasant stranger", and knowing only too well what her brother is likely to do, tries to dissuade him from harming the visitor.

"What I am paid for, I do," declares her brother. "He is probably asleep now. Go to his room and bring me his sword." As Maddelene returns with the sword, Gilda approaches the door. She is now in the costume of a youth with riding boots and spurs. She has been drawn back in spite of herself and arrives just in time to hear Maddelene beg her brother not to murder the "nice young man". Their conversation reveals to Gilda that her own father has paid the assassin to do this deed.

Won by further pleading from Maddelene, Sparafucile grudgingly agrees to spare the Duke if some other man arrives before midnight whom he can substitute as a victim. He makes the promise easily, confident that on such a stormy night no other guest will make his way to this deserted spot.

Forgiving the Duke for his faithlessness, Gilda decides to sacrifice herself for him. Maddelene and Sparafucile are startled at her knock but hastily arrange for the gruesome welcome. As Gilda enters, she is struck down.

Her father appears punctually at midnight and the assassin delivers

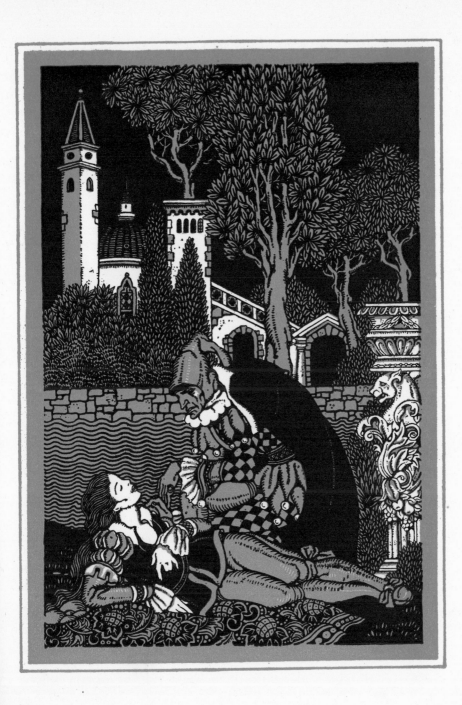

the sack which Rigoletto, to satisfy his thirst for vengeance, has determined to cast into the river himself. As he starts off with his burden he is thunderstruck to hear the voice of the Duke, who has now awakened and is humming the refrain of his song, *La donna è mobile.*

Rigoletto, now wild with fear, tears open the sack and finds his beloved daughter, mortally wounded. His cries of anguish arouse the dying girl. She smiles faintly when she recognizes her father. Then, summoning her failing strength, she reveals that she has sacrificed herself to save the Duke whom she still loves. She implores her father to forgive her, and dies in his arms.

Thus did a father's curse descend on Rigoletto.

THE
BARBER *of* SEVILLE
or
THE
GOOD-NATURED BUSYBODY
by GIOACHINO ROSSINI

The Barber of Seville

IN this merry opera by Rossini, a barber named Figaro is given the
honor of the title role. The story takes us to the romantic Spanish
city of Seville at a time (about two hundred years ago) when
Figaro, or someone very much like him, was a well-known character
—a good-natured busybody who loved to pry into other people's affairs.

In those days there were no learned doctors or dentists as we have
them today and a barber who could wield shears and razor skillfully
would be called upon to perform other "operations" as well. It was not
at all unusual for him to pull a tooth for a suffering customer or to
make an incision in his arm, since, at that time, bleeding was the
approved way of treating many illnesses. In order to advertise their
surgical accomplishments barbers placed a red and white pole outside
their shops to symbolize a bleeding arm done up in a white bandage.
Even now barbers still use this ancient sign of their craft, although they
no longer perform surgical or dental operations.

Figaro was an artist in his line and he did not hesitate to admit it, but
he was so witty and nimble-fingered and such a likeable and good-
natured fellow that he was a general favorite.

Old Dr. Bartolo was a wealthy and prominent citizen of Seville at
that time and he was also the guardian of a fascinating young girl named
Rosina. Although the Doctor had a fine house and many servants, and
Rosina was rich in her own right, she was not happy. Her guardian was
both miserly and disagreeable and, moreover, he kept an eagle eye on
her at all times. Rosina, who longed to be gay and merry, did not love
her guardian and, in fact, considered him a rather stupid old man.
Affairs have recently come to a climax for the old Doctor has asked
Rosina to marry him and she has flatly refused to do so. He has since
been making life even more miserable for her. He now refuses to let her
out of his sight if he can help it and is consumed with jealousy if she
looks at a younger man.

One evening Rosina has a thrilling experience. She notices a good-
looking young cavalier—apparently someone of high station—who
openly admires her and follows her at a respectful distance as she walks
slowly homeward. She is accompanied by the elderly Berta who is her
maid and constant companion since in those days a young girl of good

family never appeared on the streets alone. Rosina is beginning to wonder if she will ever see her "Unknown" again when she discovers him in the street below her balcony early one morning.

It is Rosina's habit to come out on this balcony to enjoy the early morning air, and her admirer has discovered this. In fact he has been haunting the house day and night ever since his first glimpse of her. He and Rosina have often seen each other in this romantic fashion and have enjoyed a little harmless flirtation. But they have never been able to get farther than a hurried greeting without the interference of the old Doctor.

In desperation, Rosina has written a note to her "Unknown" and plans to drop it over the balcony the next time he appears. This is the situation when the opera begins, and even before the curtain rises the bright and tuneful music in the overture prepares one for a most entertaining time.

Theme from the Overture

The opening scene shows the house of Dr. Bartolo in the dim light of early dawn. Fiorello, a servant of the rich young Count Almaviva, appears. (The Count is Rosina's unknown admirer.) His servant is carrying a lantern and is much occupied trying to keep a band of players quiet as he groups them under Rosina's window. They have been engaged by his master for a serenade. The Count himself now appears and the players tune up and begin to play an accompaniment to the Count's song.

Smiling in the Eastern Sky (Ecco redente)

The song ended, there is no sign that Rosina has heard it for the
shutters remain closed. The Count dismisses his servant and the players
and remains there alone. His sentimental thoughts are interrupted by the
arrival of Figaro, the barber, who is lightly strumming a guitar.

"Bah! I wonder who that is, now!" mutters the Count, realizing that
his chances of talking to Rosina are dwindling. He hides behind a tree
while Figaro plays a few chords and breaks into a jolly song in which
he tells all about himself . . . . what a good fellow he is . . . . how
it is "Figaro here" and "Figaro there" and "Ho! Figaro" from everywhere. He even boasts that the world could not live or love or laugh
without him!

I am the city's factotem (Largo al factotem)

The Count, after watching a few moments, recognizes the good-
natured barber and calls to him. Figaro exclaims in surprise, "Why,
your Lordship! What are you doing in Seville?"

"Hush-sh! Perhaps this accidental meeting means that you can help
me," says the Count. "I see you seem to have prospered here," noting
his spruce appearance.

"On starvation!" is Figaro's glib reply.

"The same old rascal, I see," smiles his companion giving him a tip.
The Count, who is one of the most powerful grandees of Spain, now
tells Figaro that no one else in Seville knows his real identity and certain
matters have transpired to make him wish to remain unknown for a
short time longer. He is interested in a "flower of beauty" whom he
saw one evening on the Prado and whom he followed to this very house.
The Count admits that he longs to know the young lady better, but
without revealing his social status. For the time being he prefers to be
known merely as "Signor Lindoro", a person of no consequence.

"She is evidently the daughter of the crusty old Doctor who lives
here," observes the Count.

"Daughter? No indeed!" Figaro replies, "She's the old gentleman's ward, and rich besides. He, poor old fool, is trying to make her marry him and he keeps her almost a prisoner. She doesn't want him, though. I know that!" Figaro explains.

"Then you are allowed to enter there?" asks the Count with great interest.

"I should say I am," Figaro assures him. "I am called there every day or two to shave the old man, or to carry a message for the pretty Miss."

"Then you really can help me," exclaims the Count, delighted. "If you can think up some way for me to get in to see her without telling her who I am, you will be richly rewarded." Glancing up, they see the door to the balcony opening and they hide nearby as Rosina comes out.

"Oh dear! He isn't here," she says, disappointed. The Count, without quite showing himself (not being sure that Rosina is alone), goes through an agonized dumb show to try to attract her attention. "How provoking!" Rosina continues, talking to herself. "I wanted to give him this note." Just then she catches sight of her admirer but at that instant the vigilant old Doctor spoils everything by coming out on the balcony. Rubbing his hands and putting on a genial smile he greets his ward.

"Well, my dear, enjoying the fine morning air, I see." Then he observes the note in her hand and his expression changes. "What is that paper?" he asks crossly.

Rosina drops the note over the balcony. "Oh, too bad!" she exclaims, pretending to be quite put out. "It blew out of my hand. It had the words of an aria I am studying."

"I will see whether or not you are telling the truth, Miss," cries her guardian disappearing within. By the time he gets down to the street the Count has already picked up the fluttering paper (knowing it to be intended for him) and is out of sight. Dr. Bartolo flies into a rage when he cannot find it and declares that Rosina has been up to some trick again. "It would not be the first time," he thunders as he disappears inside the house.

The Count, to his great joy, learns from the note that Rosina trusts him enough to ask that he help her to escape from her guardian's strict control. Dr. Bartolo now reappears with hat and cane and tells a servant not to admit anyone on any pretext whatsoever except Don Basilio, the music-master.

No sooner is he out of sight than the Count, borrowing Figaro's guitar, pours out his heart in a song to Rosina; and this time she hears him.

Who 'neath thy window sighing (Se il mio nome saper)

In the song he tells her he is "Lindoro" and poor, and that his devoted love is all he can give her. Rosina, thrilled by his song, leans over the balcony, throws him a rose, and then ventures to say, "If Lindoro really loves me, why does he not . . . ." but runs off the balcony without finishing her sentence.

"I *must* get in to talk to her," declares the Count, much excited. "She is adorable! Figaro, you must think up some way to do it." Figaro blandly hints that he can always think better with money in his pocket. The Count obligingly thrusts a well filled purse into his hand and tells him there will be more if he succeeds in helping him.

Figaro now recalls that a visiting regiment of cavalry is due this day and that many of the large homes will be requisitioned for temporary lodgings. "You can disguise yourself as the Colonel of the regiment," suggests Figaro. "Then come to Dr. Bartolo's house armed with a fake requisition for lodgings and demand admission. After that, it is for you to find an opportunity to talk with your young lady."

"Leave that to me," says the Count confidently, agreeing to the plan.

The next scene shows Rosina in her own room. When the curtain rises she is seated at her desk finishing a love-letter to her "Lindoro." In the following song (one of the most famous of soprano arias), she tells how his name is already "enshrined" in her heart.

A little voice I heard (Una voce poco fa)

Rosina's one concern is to find a way to get her letter to her lover. As if in answer to her need, Figaro is announced. The barber pretends to have come to shave the Doctor (who is away) but he is really there to talk with Miss Rosina about "Signor Lindoro" and to let her know the plan for him to appear in the guise of a Colonel. Figaro has not had time to tell her this before the old Doctor comes stumping in. The barber leaps behind a screen but as the scene progresses he peeks out from time to time and his comical expression shows that he is taking in everything that is being said.

The Doctor, suspicious as usual, bombards Rosina with questions. "Has anyone been here?" he asks. "That rascal, Figaro, perhaps? A quack of a barber!" Rosina, watching him from the back, says in a low voice, "There he goes, always scolding about someone!"

"Rosina," calls the Doctor, raising his voice, "have you seen him?"

"Seen whom?" asks Rosina in an innocent voice, just to be provoking.

"The barber, Figaro!" explains her guardian with exasperation.

"Yes, he was here for a few minutes. I always find him amusing," says Rosina saucily and leaves the room.

"Pert, as usual," growls her guardian while Figaro shows by his grimaces how much he is enjoying the situation.

Dr. Bartolo's arch-conspirator, Don Basilio, now arrives. He calls himself a "music-master" but he is not much of a musician. He is a large lumbering man and a malicious gossip, his true "art" being that of minding other people's business. It is this unpleasant man whom the Doctor has engaged to spy upon his ward. Don Basilio, bowing low, announces that he has news. He has found out that a certain young man is spending much time in this vicinity and has even made the acquaintance of Miss Rosina. He is trying to keep his identity a secret, but Basilio has discovered that he is the powerful Grandee, Count Almaviva.

This sends the old Doctor into a paroxysm of jealous fury and Don Basilio advises his employer to spread malicious slander about the young man which will drive him from the city. At this even Dr. Bartolo demurs. "That would be defamation of character," he says. "That is dangerous! No! My plan is best. I will marry Rosina, myself, at once. That will keep other suitors away." Drawing Don Basilio's arm through his, the Doctor continues, "Come, we'll see about this now," and leads him from the room.

"Whew!" exclaims Figaro, coming out from behind the screen. "It's lucky I overheard their plans. Now we know how fast to work!"

"What news, Figaro?" asks Rosina, tripping in. He tells her of her guardian's plan to marry her at once, whether she wishes to or not. "Pooh! Ridiculous!" sniffs Rosina. She then brings the conversation around to the events of that morning and asks Figaro about the young man who had been with him—wishing, of course, to know more about her admirer.

"Oh, he is a cousin of mine named Lindoro," Figaro says casually. "Poor fellow! I feel so sorry for him. He is desperately in love but doesn't know how the young lady in question regards him."

"Who is she?" demands Rosina, trying to sound indifferent. Figaro makes her drag from him, bit by bit, the information that it is she, herself, whom "Cousin Lindoro" admires. The barber suggests that it would greatly please his "cousin" to receive a message from her. Rosina pretends to hesitate, then, shame-facedly holds out to Figaro the letter she has already written!

"Oh, these precious women!" cries Figaro in comic astonishment. "One cannot keep up with them!" He promises to deliver the love letter and tells Rosina she may count on seeing "Lindoro" soon. In his hurry to go, however, he fails to inform her about the disguise they have planned.

Rosina's guardian soon comes back and he and his niece are again in a heated argument when a peremptory knocking is heard. When Berta, the aged housekeeper, answers the door, there stands a cavalry officer, followed by his men. In a commanding tone he demands admittance, showing his official requisition.

"What! You get out of here!" shouts the Doctor. "My house is exempt!" A comical scene ensues in which the "Colonel" insists that orders are orders and the Doctor insists he will hold to his rights in his own house. They both grow more and more insistent. The Doctor is very angry and the Count pretends to be equally so. He is playing for time in the hope that Rosina will appear. She does come in at last and he manages to whisper to her that he is "Lindoro" and that he has a note for her in his hand. They both watch for a moment when the Doctor is not looking. Then the Count lets the letter fall to the floor and Rosina drops her handkerchief over it. The Count, of course, gallantly picks up the "handkerchief" to hand it to Miss Rosina but the Doctor, ever suspicious, sees him do this and demands, "What is he giving you?"

Prepared for just such an emergency, Rosina shows her guardian a laundry list which she says she dropped and the Doctor is somewhat non-plussed. By this time his loud voice has attracted a crowd to the front of the house where the "Colonel's" soldiers are waiting for admittance. In the midst of it all Figaro, who has been waiting to appear when needed, comes in with his shaving basin under his arm. Rosina sighs with relief when she sees the barber because she is a little frightened at the way things are turning out. To make matters worse, the police arrive to investigate the cause of the disturbance.

At Dr. Bartolo's request they surround the "Colonel" to arrest him as a disturber of the peace, but he draws the police officer to one side and shows him the insignia of his rank. The police at once salute and withdraw to the great astonishment of everyone. Deciding that explanations might prove inconvenient, the Count departs accompanied by his men and Figaro. Rosina is left to wonder what it is all about, and the Doctor to recover from the excitement.

Since the scheme of impersonating the Colonel has failed, the Count and Figaro now devise another ruse, and it is this new plot which brings about the amusing situation in the next act.

When the curtain rises, it shows the drawing-room in Dr. Bartolo's house on the day of Rosina's music lesson. The Doctor is in the room alone and is still angry at the intrusion of the Colonel. In spite of many inquiries the old gentleman has not been able to establish the Colonel's identity and has concluded that he was probably sent as an emissary by "that Count Almaviva" to learn Rosina's sentiments. "This goes to prove," thinks the Doctor, "that no one is safe even in his own house. But they won't fool me!" he adds with great satisfaction.

The Doctor now goes to answer a knock at the door without waiting for a servant, and admits a young man (the Count in disguise) in the black gown of a music-master. He pays his respects to the old gentleman and explains that he is "Don Alonzo", a student of the music-master, Don Basilio. He further explains that since his master is ill he has been sent to give the lesson to Miss Rosina.

Dr. Bartolo is mistrustful although he does not recognize "Don Alonzo" in this disguise. To win the confidence of Rosina's guardian, the Count hits upon the idea of giving Dr. Bartolo the letter Rosina has written to her "Lindoro" and secretly enjoys the old man's rage. Pursuing his advantage, he ingratiates himself further by inventing the story that he has "found" the note by accident. He says moreover that if he can have a word with Miss Rosina he is confident that he can make her mistrust her new admirer. The Doctor thinks this is a capital plan and calls his ward to come for her lesson. She gasps when she sees who the "music-master" is, but quickly hides her surprise with a cough.

"Seat yourself by my side, fair lady," says the disguised Count, indicating the bench at the piano, "and I will give you your music lesson."

"Oh, sir! with the greatest of pleasure," replies Rosina.

"What will you sing for me?" asks the "music-master".

"Whatever you wish me to sing, sir," says Rosina sweetly. She selects a piece of music and opens it on the rack as the "master" nods approval.

"Now then, sing with spirit," commands "Don Alonzo", with pretended sternness, playing the opening measures of the accompaniment to Rosina's song.

This is the famous "lesson scene" of the opera and it is at this point that the prima donna who takes the part of Rosina introduces any song or aria she wishes to use as an exhibition piece. This custom came about through the loss of the original aria which Rossini composed and which was never found after the first few performances of the opera. Since that time each artist interpreting the role of Rosina uses this opportunity to sing a favorite "show piece" in her repertoire.

"Bravissimo! A fine voice, truly!" exclaims the Count when Rosina has finished.

"A thousand thanks, sir," says Rosina smiling.

"Yes, Yes! A fine voice," acknowledges Dr. Bartolo testily, "but in my day they sang other songs." In a cracked voice he makes a comical effort to sing a popular air. Figaro, with his shaving-basin under his arm, now appears in the doorway and dares to mimic his distinguished client. The old gentleman takes this in good part, however, since Figaro is about the only person in the world who can bully him, and asks mildly enough, "Well, you rascal, what did you come for?"

"I?" demands Figaro, pretending astonishment. "Why, to shave you, of course. This is your day." The Doctor tries to put off this important engagement but Figaro is firm. He has promised the Count to be there to keep Rosina's guardian busy so that "Alonzo" can talk with his "pupil".

"Oh, very well, then," sighs the Doctor with resignation. He gives his huge bunch of house-keys to Figaro and tells him to fetch the towels. This is just what that rascal has wanted and as he passes Rosina he whispers, "Which key unlocks the lattice to your balcony?"

"The newest one," Rosina replies much excited. "Lindoro" (now pretending to be "Alonzo") has not yet had a chance to tell her that everything has been arranged for a midnight elopement and wedding, but she senses that great plans are on foot.

Dr. Bartolo seats himself in a large chair at the end of the room farthest from the piano and Figaro tucks in the towels, lathers his face, and tries his best to monopolize his customer's attention by his chatter.

In spite of all this, the old gentleman, his face covered with lather, gets up more than once to have a look at master and pupil.

The Count, who is still "Lindoro" to Rosina, explains that he and Figaro will come for her at midnight. They will then take her to Figaro's home where a notary will be waiting to marry them. He plays a few chords now and then, to hide the fact that the "lesson" is not progressing at all, and Rosina sings her scales. Everything appears to be going smoothly when, to the dismay of the conspirators, Don Basilio, the real music-master, appears.

"Don Basilio," exclaims Rosina in a terrified whisper.

"He of all people," mutters the Count.

"What infernal luck," grumbles Figaro.

"But my good man, you are sick. You should be at home in bed," exclaims the Doctor who has quite believed the story "Don Alonzo" has told him. Don Basilio is speechless with bewilderment at this reception. Dr. Bartolo goes on to say that since he has a fever he should not have ventured out at all.

"A fever!" exclaims Don Basilio, looking from one to the other.

"You're as yellow as a corpse!" cries Figaro, pretending to feel his pulse.

"Do go home and take some medicine," declare Figaro and the Count together as the latter presses a purse into his hand, adding, "I am really quite alarmed about you."

"Yes, yes. Do go home," both Rosina and the Doctor implore him.

"A purse . . . . home to bed . . . . they all seem of one mind," Don Basilio mumbles to himself. As they keep crowding about him, all talking at once, he turns in an exasperated manner and says, "Since you all wish it, *I will go*." He takes his leave and is followed by a chorus of relieved good-byes from the Count, Rosina and Figaro, in which even the Doctor joins.

They all resume their former places. Figaro is still lingering over the shaving when the Count unconsciously raises his voice as he tells Rosina of their plans. Dr. Bartolo overhears him and, though he has no idea that "Don Alonzo" is the Count, he is consumed with rage to find himself tricked again. "Don Alonzo" and Figaro take their departure while Rosina goes to her room to prepare for the excitement of her midnight wedding.

Dr. Bartolo, still raging, has put on his hat and gone to see Don Basilio to find out just how he has been duped. This next act shows the two old men returning some hours later to Dr. Bartolo's house. The

Doctor has discovered that Don Basilio was not ill and now he is saying, "You do not know this Alonzo?"

"I do not." Don Basilio's tone is emphatic.

"Then he was undoubtedly sent here by that rascally Count Almaviva to carry out some plot," says the Doctor.

"But I tell you this 'Alonzo' is the Count himself!" insists Don Basilio, fingering the heavy purse in his pocket.

"If this is true, call a notary this very evening and have him draw up the contract at once for my marriage to Rosina," orders the Doctor.

"What, tonight?" exclaims his companion. "Ridiculous! It's raining in torrents, and besides, the notary has told me that he is busy tonight officiating at the marriage of Figaro's niece."

"His niece?" cries the Doctor. "The barber has no niece. This is another trick. Go! Get the notary at once and when you come back, let yourself in with this latch-key." Basilio takes the key and hurries away.

Left alone, Rosina's guardian has an inspiration. There is the letter which "Don Alonzo" has given him . . . . the letter Rosina wrote to "Lindoro". Perhaps this is a weapon he can use to his advantage. He calls his ward. "Rosina, Rosina! Come here, my child!" Rosina enters without looking up. "My darling child, I have news that will grieve you. You have placed your affections on one unworthy of you, one who laughs at your simple heart." He shows Rosina the letter.

"My letter!" exclaims Rosina. "How did you get that?"

"From Don Alonzo. He and the barber are in league against you, my dear. They are going to betray your confidence and place you in the power of a wealthy noble, Count Almaviva." The Doctor's ruse works beautifully.

"Count Almaviva!" exclaims his ward who has never heard of him. "Oh, Lindoro, are you really a traitor?" Then, suddenly angry, she resolves to pay "Lindoro's" supposed treachery in kind. "Good Doctor," says Rosina, "if you still wish to marry me, I am yours."

"How happy you make me." Her guardian is jubilant.

"We must be married at once!" cries poor Rosina. "Do not delay. At midnight Don Alonzo and Figaro are coming to take me away."

"The scoundrels!" shouts the Doctor. "I will lock all the doors."

"That will do no good." Rosina speaks breathlessly. "They have the key to the balcony and are planning to enter by the window."

"Then I will summon the police and have them arrested," declares her guardian. Weeping, Rosina leaves the room. Her dream of happiness has vanished.

The curtain rising on the last act shows Rosina's bedchamber. It is midnight and the room is in semi-darkness. It is storming outside as the Count and Figaro enter by the window. Both are wrapped in long black cloaks. Figaro, who is preceding the Count, carries a lighted lantern. "One more step and we are here," he says.

"Great Neptune! What a night!" exclaims the Count, climbing over the sill.

"It is lovers' weather," says Figaro by way of consolation.

"Where is Rosina?" asks the Count, peering anxiously into the dark room. "Ah, here you are, my darling," he says as Rosina approaches. To his utter amazement she repels his advances.

"Your base designs are known to me, sir," she says in a voice which she vainly strives to render hard. "I trusted you, and . . . ." She hesitates, near to tears.

"I do not understand," exclaims the Count.

"It's utterly beyond me," mutters Figaro.

"Silence, you pretender!" cries Rosina. "You have planned to place me in the power of your base employer, Count Almaviva!"

"Oh, so that is it." The Count's voice expresses infinite relief. He thereupon falls to his knees and explains that "Lindoro" and the Count are one and the same.

"Oh, how happy I am!" sighs Rosina as the Count embraces her. They are so absorbed in each other that they pay no heed to Figaro's warning to hurry. The barber then goes to look over the balcony and returns to say that two men with lanterns are in front of the house. This cuts off their exit by the door. The only, and very romantic, escape is by way of the window.

Let us fly by yonder window (Zitti, zitti)

Figaro starts first but stops with an exclamation. "Now we *are* in for it," he says. "Someone has taken the ladder away." While they are still trying to decide what to do, Don Basilio appears with the notary. He calls for Dr. Bartolo whom he expects to find there, but receives no answer. "It is Basilio," whispers Figaro to the Count.

"Who is the other man?" asks Almaviva.

"Oh joy!" Figaro's voice expresses relief. "My friend, the notary. Leave everything to me!" Stepping forward, he greets the notary. "Good evening, my good sir. You remember you were to officiate tonight at the wedding of my niece and the Count Almaviva. The young couple have met here by chance. Have you the necessary papers with you?"

The notary takes a document from his pocket, but while he is looking it over, Don Basilio remarks, "We must go slowly here. Does Dr. Bartolo know of this?"

"Ah, Don Basilio," interrupts the Count, taking him to one side. "Here is a ring." He draws a valuable jewel from his finger and presents it to Don Basilio. "Pray accept this as a token of my friendship."

"But . . . . but . . . ." Basilio hesitates.

"Pray keep it!" says the Count in a determined tone, "or you may have a bullet in your head."

"In that case," says Basilio blandly, "who signs this paper?"

"All who are here," declares the Count first signing it himself. In a few minutes the brief ceremony is over and a second later Dr. Bartolo arrives—with the police. It was he who had removed the ladder. He points to Figaro and the Count. "Those men are robbers. Do your duty."

"All in good time, sir," says the officer in charge, and, turning to the Count, asks his name.

"My name has never been questioned," states the Count. "This lady, my wife . . . ."

"Your wife!" sputters the Doctor. "Confound your impudence! Rosina, you are going to marry me tonight!"

"Marry *you?*" laughs Rosina. "Don't be ridiculous!" The Doctor wrathfully demands an explanation—and gets too much for they all talk at once. He finally learns that, once again, his pert and pretty ward has outwitted him. He is somewhat mollified by the Count's assurance that he does not expect a marriage dot and finally gives the two his blessing while Figaro looks on with delight at the happy outcome.

THE RHINEGOLD
or
THE
STOLEN TREASURE
by RICHARD WAGNER

(First Opera of The Nibelung's Ring)

The Rhinegold

ZOO-OO-OOM-M-M. The low strings of the orchestra sound a deep "ground tone" and keep it vibrating—on and on and on. The tone sounds like the unceasing movement of deep waters, the steady flow of a mighty river.

Presently a soft, undulating rhythm is heard suggesting the gentle waves of surface water. As this becomes bolder and more clear, it sweeps us up and up, out of the depths to the surface of the river. The orchestra paints in music an accurate picture of what we see when the curtain goes up on the first act of this opera.

At first it is dark, but as the undulating rhythm grows more brisk, the scene lightens to reveal the rocky shore of the River Rhine and three maidens who swim about, playing a kind of hide-and-seek with each other. They are the Rhine-maidens who live in the depths of the river with nothing to do but watch over a nugget of gold, the "Rhinegold", hidden in a cleft of the rocks. Wotan, chief of all the gods, had long ago set them at this task and had warned them never to reveal the treasure to anyone, since the Rhinegold, if stolen from its hiding-place, would bring untold woe into the world. . . . .

The Rhinegold is the first of four operas which Richard Wagner composed as one continuous story to comprise his great cycle known as The Nibelung's Ring. The other three operas are The Valkyrie or Die Walküre, Siegfried, and The Twilight of the Gods or Die Götterdämmerung.

The story of The Nibelung's Ring is placed in the long-forgotten time when the earth was thought to be inhabited by four different races: the gods and goddesses who occupied the topmost mountain peaks and the cloud regions above; the giants, strong and stupid, who lived lower down on the mountains and performed heavy labor for the gods; men and women—human beings like ourselves—who inhabited the plains and forests; and last, an ugly race of dwarfs called Nibelungs, who lived in dark caves underneath the surface of the earth.

All lived their own lives and seldom interfered with each other. Each group led an existence suited to its own tastes and needs, and, since there

was nothing one possessed that any of the others wanted, the world was at peace.

Wotan, chief of the gods, was both wise and shrewd. He knew well the potential power of the Rhinegold and for that reason he had given it to the Rhine-maidens for safe-keeping. As long as it rested in the rocky cleft by the bank of the river, it remained a harmless bit of beautiful gold. But once this treasure fell into unscrupulous hands, it would become a power for evil, a violent destructive force to loose upon the world a Pandora's box of hatred and greed.

Wotan, who knew the legend of the gold, was quite aware that he who acquired it would also acquire the ability to fashion a part of the yellow metal into a magic Helmet and the rest into a Ring that would give him untold wealth and power. The wearer of this Ring could become master of the world and even threaten the might and glory of the gods. Wotan had no use for the gold himself, since he already reigned as a supreme being, but he naturally did not wish to have anyone else have it. For this reason he hid the Rhinegold in the river and felt that all would be well.

Wotan had been careful in his instructions to the Rhine-maidens and had cautioned them never to let any stranger so much as lay his hands upon the gold. He explained to them that it could be wrested from its hiding place only by someone who had renounced all love and happiness for the sake of the power the gold would bring him. It was not at all likely, the Rhine-maidens thought, that anyone in the world could be so stupid as to imagine life worth living without love and happiness. Therefore they, too, felt safe and guarded their treasure without fear.

When the curtain goes up on the first act of the opera the three Rhine-maidens are swimming about in the depths of the river and singing any nonsense that comes into their heads.

Song of the Rhine-maidens

Suddenly a grotesque creature comes sliding and slithering down the rocks to the water's edge. It is the ugly dwarf Alberich, Prince of the Nibelungs, who dwell in the dark and slimy caves under the earth. He watches the Rhine-maidens at play with gloating eyes and presently calls to one of them.

"Come here, pretty creature. Let me kiss you!"

All three break into laughter at his daring and Flosshilde swims close to him, but just as he tries to catch her, she darts away.

"Come and catch me if you can," Wellgunde, one of her sisters, taunts him, "I am prettier than she is!" Alberich makes a desperate lunge, misses her, and almost falls into the water. They shout merrily over his predicament while Woglinde, the third of the Rhine-maidens, says teasingly, "Why not woo me?"

Their playfulness soon leads to a game of catch-as-catch-can. Alberich scrambles wildly up and down the slippery rocks, chasing first one and then another of the lovely maidens. As they mock him they fail to notice that he is rapidly growing angry and more and more determined to get his hands on one of them.

The rays of the sun now light the waters of the river and a strong beam, shining directly upon the rock, strikes the gold and makes it glitter. Seeing this, Flosshilde and her sisters forget everything else and swim back and forth in front of the Rhinegold Rock, singing joyfully to their treasure. Now, for the first time, the "gold theme" is played by the orchestra, and is heard again whenever the gold, in its innocent, harmless state, is mentioned.

The Gold Theme

The Rhine-maidens have quite forgotten Alberich who stands on the bank watching them. Now he turns his gaze toward the glittering treasure to which their song is directed. "Tell me, you slippery creatures, what gleams and glows there in the sunlight?" he asks.

"Where do you hail from, stupid one, not to have heard of the Rhinegold?" they ask, astonished.

Flosshilde warns her sisters. "Sh-h. You know Wotan told us never to mention the Rhinegold to anyone."

"What nonsense!" argues Woglinde. "There is no danger. Foolish Alberich dotes on us. See how he eyes us. He would never want the gold!"

"Do not be too sure," Flosshilde warns, but her sisters pay no heed. Babbling idly, they tell Alberich all about the Rhinegold, and that he who possesses it can make a Ring which will give him power to rule the world.

"We know this means nothing to you," they say laughing. "Only he who gives up all desire for love will have strength to tear the gold from the rock!" While they are describing the power of the Ring, the ominous "Ring theme" is heard in the orchestra. How different it is from the innocent "gold theme"!

The Ring Theme

Alberich has listened intently to what they say, and, infuriated by their teasing, he suddenly determines to be avenged. This gold, if it truly has this power, is worth the taking. He gives vent to his thoughts in a torrent of wrath and curses his tormentors. Then, shouting that they had better guard their treasure, he clambers in desperate haste to the Rhinegold Rock and, with a mighty tug, loosens the gleaming nugget. In another moment he holds it in his hands, and before the startled Rhine-maidens realize what has happened, he has climbed the bank and disappeared.

The depths of the Rhine are cast into gloom when the gold is stolen. The atmosphere grows dark and we hear above the steady flowing of the river the sad song of the Rhine-maidens lamenting the loss of their treasure.

Richard Wagner planned this opera to be produced without any break between the acts. For this purpose he wrote long interludes of music so that, during the transition from one scene to another while the stage is shrouded in darkness, the orchestra weaves a continuous tone picture of the change of scene which is taking place. The composer has supplied simple themes which might be called "musical labels", for every important character and object in the story. If one knows these themes, the music of the opera becomes very clear and easy to follow.

When Alberich steals the gold, the Rhine scene is ended. The orchestra continues to play and presently the river music ceases and new sounds and rhythms gradually dominate. The listener is conducted—almost as though blindfolded—into the upper regions. As the stage grows light, the orchestra breaks into a majestic chord progression which represents the castle of the gods, called Valhalla.

The Valhalla Theme

The scene shows a flowery meadow near the summit of a mountain in the lofty realm of the gods. Wotan, chief of the gods, lies sleeping, and nearby is his wife, Fricka. She awakes as the sun rises and almost at once sees the wonderful castle, Valhalla, rising above the clouds. The towers and turrets, roseate in the early morning light, are a glittering monument to the glory of the gods.

Fricka speaks quickly. "Wake up, wake up, my lord! See this fulfillment of your dreams."

Wotan, majestic in stature and bearing, rises to gaze upon this mighty edifice and breaks forth in jubilation quite without thought of the price he must pay. He has bargained with the giants, Fafner and Fasolt, who have agreed to erect Valhalla according to his plans. In return, he has promised to give them Fricka's sister, the fair young goddess, Freia. Wotan's wife now reminds him of this promise and declares that even magnificent Valhalla is not worth such a sacrifice. Wotan knows this, too, and has no intention of holding to his side of the bargain. This is not the first time that Wotan has made a promise without intending to keep it for he does not hesitate to resort to trickery to gain his ends. Even in his youth his lust for power has led him to a deed which cost him "half of his integrity", symbolized, now, by the loss of one eye.

"Pray give no heed to that promise," he reassures Fricka. "I shall not permit our fair Freia to fall into the hands of the giants. I have sent Loki (Loge) around the earth to find something they will accept in place of her."

Just then Freia rushes in, begging them to save her from the giants who are even now on their way to claim her. Her brothers, Froh, the Rainbow God, and Donner, the Thunder God, follow quickly to protect her. At this moment the orchestra begins to play the clump, clump, music which announces that the giants are coming.

The Giants' Theme

As soon as they arrive they remind Wotan that their task is finished. "Up there stands your glorious castle, built according to your plans," they say. "Now we demand the payment."

Instead of promptly fulfilling his agreement as the giants expect him to do, Wotan hesitates. The honest giants are at first speechless with amazement that a god would seek to break an agreement of honor. Then their fury rises.

"How dare you, Son of Light, forget your promise?" demands Fasolt. "More wise you are than we are wary, but cursed be your wisdom and peace flee from you, if you fail to keep the pact. Thus speaks a stupid giant to a god. Be warned by him!"

Freia cries out in dismay at this outburst and her brothers threaten the giants. Wotan lamely seeks to quiet them.

"How sly you are," he says to the giants, "to take for earnest pledge what was but said in jest. I have changed my mind. You must accept other wage than Freia!"

"You flout us, then?" the giants shout, advancing to take Freia away by force, but Froh and Donner hold them back and Wotan mutters to himself, "I wonder where Loki stays." For Wotan has counted upon Loki, the Fire God, to help him out of this predicament. Loki who is cynical and unscrupulous, is also shrewd and brilliant, and Wotan places great faith in his counsel.

"Why do you depend on such a rascal?" demands Fricka.

But Wotan defends him, "He has aided me many a time, and Loki's help is always of greatest worth when he dallies longest." While he speaks, the orchestra begins to play the Loki music which sounds like flickering fire.

The Loki Theme

Loki comes leaping in and his flame-colored garments fly wildly about him. Rather contemptuous of the slow-moving Wotan, the Fire God delights in prolonging the suspense. As all crowd about him, he shakes them off and takes his time to answer their impatient questions. Loki loves to hear himself talk.

He now begins by praising the work of the giants. He explains that he has himself tested every nook and cranny of Valhalla, every tower and turret, and has found the castle an excellent piece of construction.

"We know all this," Wotan breaks in angrily. Then, in a low aside to Loki, Wotan continues, "When I pretended to agree that the giants should be paid with the gift of our beloved Freia, you promised to find a way out."

"I merely promised to try," sneers Loki.

"See what a deceitful scamp he is," cries Fricka. "Why do you trust him?"

"Loki is your name," shouts Froh, "but 'liar' would suit you better!"

"Ingratitude is always my reward," complains Loki.

"Be patient, I beg you all," urges Wotan, "and listen to what he would tell us."

Loki now describes how he has girdled the globe and has inquired everywhere among men of high and low degree what they hold most precious. The answer has always been the same. "Love and beauty are life's greatest treasures. No one can be happy without love."

Then Loki says that he has visited the Rhine-maidens who have told him that they have lost the Rhinegold. This disturbs Wotan for he has not heard of the theft of the gold. When Loki continues with a description of the thief and says that he is Alberich, the Nibelung, even the giants prick up their ears.

At the mention of the cruel dwarf they look at each other. "Alberich!" they exclaim, "an old enemy of ours." And they ask Loki:

"What is there in this gold that makes the wily Alberich desire it?"

"He desires it because it is the symbol of all earthly power," Loki replies. "But only the man who gives up all thought of love for the sake of the gold's power can use it to fashion a Ring which will make him master of the world!"

For the first time Wotan's supremacy is threatened. He says:

"I, too, have heard of the strange power of the Ring. I am the one who should own it!"

"You are too late," laughs Loki. "Alberich is already wearing it. It is the Nibelung's Ring now! Throughout the whole of his underground kingdom, Nibelheim, millions of slaves are toiling to pile up greater and greater riches and power for him. It is more than likely that his clutching fingers will one day reach even to Valhalla!"

The brother giants, Fafner and Fasolt, have been in deep consultation. Now they suggest to Wotan, "Suppose we accept this gold in place of Freia? It would make us rich and powerful."

"But how can I give it to you when it is not mine to give?" demands Wotan.

"Remedy that by getting it," suggests Loki. "It takes a thief to rob a thief." He enjoys taunting Wotan who ponders over this with his eyes cast down. At last he comes to a decision.

"I must have the Nibelung's Ring!" Wotan declares. "Up, Loki! Come with me!"

"Shall we journey to Nibelheim by way of the Rhine?" inquires Loki.

"No, not that way," objects Wotan who wishes to avoid the lamenting Rhine-maidens.

"Then we can take our way down through this brimstone gorge," Loki suggests. He goes quickly ahead and Wotan follows him.

The giants insist upon keeping Freia as hostage, promising that no harm shall come to her and that she will be set free as soon as Wotan gives them the Rhinegold.

Down, down, and down go Wotan and Loki. They are on their way to the dark realm where the Nibelungs dwell, slaving under the heartless whip-hand of Alberich.

This is another of the musical interludes. Again the music changes completely with the changing of the scene and a new theme is heard which grows louder and louder as the two conspirators near the regions of Nibelheim. The music represents the heavy monotonous labor of the weary dwarfs.

The Toil Theme

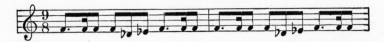

Arriving at their destination, Wotan and Loki see hordes of Nibelungs bent under great packs which weigh them down until they shriek in agony. Alberich drives them on and his whip cracks over one and then another of his subjects. The Prince of the Nibelungs stops in amazement when he sees his unexpected visitors, and then snarls at them, asking why they have come.

Wotan is wearing his disguise of "The Wanderer", a sky-blue mantle and a broad-brimmed hat which almost hides his sightless eye. He carries his ancient world-governing spear without which he never leaves Valhalla. Now he speaks mildly, pretending friendliness.

"Strange news of magic marvels has come from Nibelheim. These wonders we have come to see."

Alberich is suspicious. "Whoever you are," he replies ungraciously, "you probably covet this rich kingdom of mine. Nothing but envy and greed brings you here."

"Oh, come now," Loki breaks in. "A friend to you, miserable dwarf, am I. Look on me. Can you not trust Loki? Long ago I brought you fire and heat. Of what use would your anvils be, could you not heat your forge?"

"I know you for a cheating rogue, but I need fear nothing from your hands," boasts their host. "Here you see me entrenched!"

"Power has given you a brave spirit," remarks Loki, and then he slyly works upon Alberich's vanity by admiring the size of the piled-up treasure.

"That is a mere driblet, only the labor of today," boasts the Nibelung. "Tomorrow the hoard will be much larger. Soon I shall be master of the world—and then my first victims will be the gods who dwell in Valhalla!"

At this threat Wotan can scarcely control himself, but hides his anger. Loki hints that he does not believe in Alberich's boast of power and the dwarf stupidly begins to show off. He tells them that the magic helmet he wears at his belt, forged for him out of a bit of the Rhinegold, when placed on his head enables him to turn into any kind of terrifying monster. Loki makes believe to scoff at this.

"Just watch me! What shall it be?" asks the braggart.

"Whatever you will, but make me mute with surprise," is Loki's answer.

Alberich claps the helmet on his head and is instantly transformed into a writhing serpent. Wotan and Loki pretend to be badly frightened. This delights the dwarf who now removes the helmet and appears again in his own shape.

"I can make myself small, too," he boasts. "Nothing is simpler." Again Loki leads him on by declaring this to be unbelievable. In the next instant Alberich disappears and a small toad hops on the ground before them. At once Wotan steps upon the toad and Loki snatches the now tiny helmet from its head. Alberich is immediately changed back to his own shape and finds himself a prisoner in the strong clutches of his unwelcome visitors.

They drag him away, writhing and shrieking, and finally reach again the flowery meadow on the high plateau with Valhalla in the background. Wotan commands Alberich to use the power of his Ring (which the dwarf is still wearing) to order his slaves to bring him gold—enough to make a pile so high that it will entirely cover fair Freia and hide her from sight. This is the price the giants have demanded.

Fuming with wrath, Alberich kisses the Ring, repeats an incantation, and soon a weary procession of dwarfs make their way to the mountaintop, carrying huge sacks of gold which they deposit in an ever-increasing heap.

Loki, taking from his belt the magic Helmet, throws it on the heap, saying, "This is part of the plunder," and turning to Wotan asks, "Are you content? Shall I set him free?"

Alberich utters a groan as he sees the precious Helmet added to the pile of gold, but consoles himself for he knows that the power of the Ring, still in his possession, can win it back. But his hope is short-lived. Wotan now demands that Alberich give up the Ring and reminds him that he won it by stealing the Rhinegold.

The dwarf cries out bitterly, "If that was sin of mine, that sin falls on me alone. But if you, a mighty god, would rashly seize the Ring, that sin of yours will fall on all things that were, and are, and ever shall be!"

"Cease your idle prating," thunders, Wotan. A furious struggle follows in which he wrests the Ring from Alberich's finger. "Back to your dark Nibelheim, you impudent earth-gnome!" he commands. "Go!"

Alberich, thus bereft of the last vestige of power which he has gained, pauses only long enough to utter a frightful prophecy. He shouts so all can hear:

> *As by a curse I first won it,*
> *Henceforth cursed be the Ring!*
> *All shall lust after its power,*
> *But none can use it for gain.*
>
> *No man can own it to gladden his life,*
> *But every possessor, by care consumed,*
> *Shall languish in endless woe.*
>
> *So "bless" I the Ring!*
> *Keep it! Guard it with care!*
> *But my curse none can escape!*

The words are ominous. The faces of Wotan and the other gods grow wan and grey. It is their first premonition of the "twilight" of extinction which will one day be their fate.

Now the clump, clump music of the giants is heard and they appear, bringing Freia with them. They view the treasure with satisfaction and mark the spot where the young goddess is to stand. She remains as calm and serene as a lovely statue while the glittering gold is piled around her, higher and higher, until she appears to be completely hidden.

"Is this enough?" Loki demands of the giants.

"No," objects Fafner. "I can still see the sheen of her lovely hair." At this the magic Helmet is placed on Freia's head. The giants examine the pile of gold still more closely.

"Hah!" cries Fasolt. "Here is a tiny chink. I can see the sparkle of one of Freia's eyes. Give us the Ring on your finger," he demands roughly, but Wotan does not reply.

Greed consumes the chief of the gods. He has resorted to trickery to gain the gold, he has taken the Ring by force, and he now intends to use its power. He stands grim and silent, heedless of the threats of the giants, deaf to the frantic pleading of Fricka and the others. And as he stands tense and motionless it grows dark—a silvery, eerie darkness. An apparition—a strange, unearthly creature now rises from the earth. In a far-away voice she says:

> All things that ever were,
> I know, and all things that e'er shall be.
> And I have come to warn you, Wotan.
> Give up that ring! Its curse will never die!
>
> Be heedful of my words. Now cast it off
> Before its curse can work its woe on you.
> I, Erda, mother of all life, have spoken.

Slowly she disappears, as mysteriously as she has come.

For a long time Wotan stands pondering and visibly shaken. At last he reaches a decision. "Here, you giants, take the Ring!" He flings it upon the glittering heap and Freia, released at last, runs joyfully toward the circle of rejoicing gods.

Fafner and Fasolt at once fall greedily upon the pile of gold and begin packing it into two huge sacks, but it is not long before they accuse each other of unfair division of the spoils.

"Halt! You greedy one. We share equally!" shouts Fasolt.

"The larger half must be mine," retorts Fafner. They grow angry, and leaving the gold, they begin to clout one another with fierce blows. Their fury grows wilder and wilder until Fafner tears up a young ash tree by the roots. Using it as a club, he fells Fasolt, his brother. . . . . All is still. Fafner fills the sacks with the golden treasure, throws in the magic Helmet and the Ring. Then, placing the great burden on his back, he staggers away without so much as a glance at the brother he has slain.

The gods stand horrified . . . . so quickly has the Ring's curse begun its deadly work!

The shining battlements of Valhalla, their castle home, can now be seen through the clouds. "I must disperse these mists," declares Donner. He calls imperiously to the storm clouds to clear the air and pounds out thunder-claps with his mighty hammer. The storm breaks fiercely, but soon crashes out its fury, leaving the early evening serene and clear. The setting sun lights up the massive towers of Valhalla with a golden haze, and a rainbow bridge stretches out before the gods, leading straight to the doors of the glorious castle.

Once again we hear the impressive march of the gods—the Valhalla music. Then, from far below, rises the plaintive song of the Rhine-maidens, "Oh, give us back our shining gold!"

Loki, last in the procession of gods, looks down the steep mountainside to the Rhine Valley and calls, "You, down there, cease your wailing. Henceworth you must revel in the glitter of the gods." A ripple of laughter greets this witty sally, then Wotan takes the hand of Fricka and proudly leads the way across the rainbow bridge. Behind them all, sly Loki pauses.

"They are silly creatures, these gods," he says to himself. "I wonder why I stay in their stupid company." He hesitates a moment, then shrugs his shoulders and slowly follows them.

The Valhalla march dies away as the gods mount higher, and at last it is only the music of the rainbow that rises triumphant as the curtain falls.

The Rainbow Theme

THE VALKYRIE
(Die Walküre)
or
THE
DISOBEDIENT GODDESS
by RICHARD WAGNER

(Second Opera of The Nibelung's Ring)

The Valkyrie

THROUGHOUT long ages Wotan, chief of all the gods, reigned supreme in Valhalla. This splendid castle, built for him by the giants, Fasolt and Fafner, was a worthy setting for the might and power of the gods. Here Wotan dwelt with Fricka, his wife, and the other gods and goddesses.

But Wotan was not at peace.

He had paid for Valhalla by giving the giants a great pile of gold, a Ring, and a Helmet all obtained by the power of the Rhinegold which Alberich, an ugly dwarf of the race of Nibelungs, had stolen from the Rhine-maidens. Wotan, in turn, had stooped to trickery to get this treasure into his own hands. He had even wrested the Nibelung's Ring from Alberich by force. The ugly dwarf had hoped to become master of the world by the power of this Ring and consequently was so enraged at Wotan that he placed a curse upon the Ring and swore to be avenged.

Wotan lived in constant dread that Alberich would one day regain possession of the Ring. He took to wandering upon the earth, often consulting Erda, the Earth-mother. He created a race of war-maidens, the Valkyries, who could fly through the air on their winged steeds. They were young and beautiful and strong, but the most beautiful and the most daring of them all was Brünnhilde, the first born, and Wotan's favorite. The duty of these war-maidens was to gather the fallen warriors from battlefields and to bring them to Valhalla. There they came to life again to form an heroic body-guard for the stronghold of the gods.

But Wotan was still fearful.

Again he took to wandering over the earth, shunning only the ancient forest in the depths of which the giant Fafner lived, guarding his treasures, the Helmet and the cursed Ring of Alberich, the Nibelung. As a further safeguard, Wotan created the race which he called Volsungs, mortals with a god-like strain. Siegmund and Sieglinde were the first Volsungs. These children came to life in a wild forest and Wotan saw to it that the girl, Sieglinde, fell into the hands of a friendly tribe who cared for her and brought her up as though she had been their own. In due time she was wooed by a fierce warrior named Hunding for whom she felt more fear than love.

The boy, Siegmund, roamed the forest with Wotan who wished him to become brave and strong. The lad honored and revered him as his Volsung father, but had no idea that he was Wotan. They often met members of other tribes in combat. Once, in the thick of such a fight, Siegmund had been separated from his Volsung father. When the boy finally returned to the rude forest hut where they had been living together, he found only an empty wolf-skin. His mysterious "father" had disappeared.

Siegmund was strong and fearless but he was unhappy. He had become an adept with spear and shield and met his enemies bravely. He also mingled with friendly tribes but, in spite of this, he was always lonely. "Woeful" he called himself. He did not know his true name.

One day, while attempting to shield a maiden in distress, Siegmund was deprived of his weapons, overpowered by the enemy, and forced to flee for his life. This incident brings us to the beginning of the opera, *The Valkyrie.*

Before the curtain goes up on the first act, we hear in the music of the orchestra the patter of raindrops on the leaves of forest trees. The rain soon falls in torrents, the thunder crashes, the storm rages furiously! Presently the music grows quieter for the storm is passing, and the curtain slowly rises.

It is night. The scene shows the interior of a rude forest dwelling which has been built around the massive trunk of a tree that stands in the center of the room and rises through the roof. At one side is a simple fire-place in which a log is burning. There is a seat nearby, a corner cupboard, and a few rude chairs about a heavy table. At another end of the room a few steps lead up to a door opening into the sleeping chamber.

The fire flickers, casting deep shadows into the corners of the room. Presently the great door at the back opens and a young man staggers in. He quickly closes the door behind him and then, as though dazed, lurches toward the fireplace and drops exhausted on the hearth. He is strongly built and handsome. His light hair is very wet and he is dressed simply in a wolf's skin and crude sandals. The heavy belt he wears is weaponless.

As he lies there, a woman in flowing white garments comes down the steps from the inner room and is startled to see the stranger stretched out on the hearth. She, too, has fair hair and is young, tall, and beautiful. She wonders who he is. And although she does not learn his identity until much later, the orchestra tells us at once by persistently playing the "Siegmund" theme.

Siegmund Theme

The woman is Sieglinde. She is now the wife of Hunding and this hut is their home.

She bends anxiously over the sleeping stranger and is happy to find that he is breathing for she has feared him dead. She is filled with compassion and the tender music that expresses this emotion is repeated many times during the first act of this opera.

Compassion Theme

Siegmund starts up, asking feebly for water. Sieglinde hastens to fill a drinking-horn and hands it to him. Soon, somewhat refreshed by the cooling drink, he thanks his hostess, fixing his eyes upon her in startled admiration. The orchestra promptly tells what he is feeling.

Love Theme

He springs up and asks where he is. Sieglinde replies, "The house and wife of Hunding bid you welcome. Tarry here until he comes."

She goes to the cupboard and fills the drinking-horn, this time with foaming mead. Having enjoyed this sustaining potion, Siegmund declares that he must be on his way for, he explains, "I am an unhappy mortal and bring ill-luck to all who befriend me." But Sieglinde hastily reassures him and begs him to await her husband's return. A moment later we hear the martial music that denotes the entrance of the fierce warrior, Hunding.

Hunding Theme

After receiving hurried explanations of Siegmund's presence, Hunding declares: "Holy is my hearth." He thus offers the simple hospitality of the house and Sieglinde prepares the evening meal.

While the three are at the table, Siegmund, in reply to questions from Hunding and Sieglinde, relates the story of his life. When he reveals that he is of the tribe of Volsungs and describes his latest adventure which has left him weaponless, he discovers that his adversaries were kinsmen of Hunding's. His host springs from his seat in a threatening manner and Siegmund, with his usual ill-luck, finds himself under the roof of an enemy.

Though excited at the presence of a foe, Hunding does not forget his position as host. He assures Siegmund that the laws of hospitality will permit his visitor to stay in safety under his roof for the night. "But," Hunding warns him fiercely, "be prepared to meet me at tomorrow's dawn. Arm yourself, for I have sworn vengeance upon the foe of my kinsmen." He picks up his shield and spear, which he had laid aside on entering, and stalks up the steps to the inner room.

Sieglinde has preceded him up the steps. Before doing so, however, she has acted strangely. Standing behind Hunding's back as he challenges Siegmund, she has made meaningful gestures toward the trunk of the great tree in an attempt to convey a message to the guest. Although Siegmund notices what she does, he cannot imagine what it means.

Left alone, Siegmund rests by the hearth and has time to reflect on the strange situation. He remembers that his father, the Volsung, had once told him that in his hour of greatest need a weapon would come to his hand. But now that that hour has come he does not know where to find such a weapon. He is more concerned, for the moment, with thoughts of the beautiful woman whose husband has made him so unwelcome. And these thoughts bring him a new happiness.

Shortly after Hunding's abrupt exit Sieglinde hurriedly returns. She is excited and explains breathlessly that she has given her husband a sleeping potion to throw him into deep slumber. She urges Siegmund to take this opportunity to escape, but he refuses. He feels that such action would be cowardly and unworthy of him. Moreover, he is already so enamored of lovely Sieglinde as to forget all danger, and he tells her so.

"Then let me tell you of a wonderful weapon which I am beginning to hope may be meant for you," she urges. "You will then be prepared for whatever comes." She now relates the story of her forced marriage to Hunding. She says that an unbidden guest had arrived at the wedding. He was majestic in bearing and wore a sky-blue mantle and a broad-brimmed hat drawn down over one sightless eye. He looked at her meaningly and with great kindness. As he did so he struck a sword up to its hilt in the trunk of this tree. Then, as silently as the stranger had come, he disappeared. "Every man present tried to draw forth the sword," she says, "but it did not yield an inch!" Sieglinde now points out the hilt to Siegmund.

"Then well I knew," she continues, "that the right hero would one day come, and that he who could draw forth this sword would also be my deliverer!"

Siegmund has listened to her tale with growing emotion. Now he clasps her in his arms. "I claim the sword—and you! I feel it. We belong to each other! By right of love fierce Hunding never had claim upon you!"

During their embrace the firelight flickers high and gleams upon the shining hilt as though the sword were calling to its master. With high elation Siegmund sings of love and the happiness which the finding of Sieglinde has brought into his lonely life.

Siegmund's Love Song

Suddenly the great door at the back swings open. The storm has passed. Moonlight floods the scene and casts its spell of silver witchery on the dripping leaves of the forest trees.

Sieglinde starts back frightened. "Did someone pass?" she cries.

"No!" Siegmund's voice is vibrant. "It is love calling to us." He now triumphantly and easily draws forth the mysterious sword, swings it on high and cries joyfully, "I name this sword 'Helpneed'!"

The Sword Theme

"Ah, now I know it was for you the stranger struck this sword into the tree," exclaims Sieglinde happily. " 'Woeful' shall no longer be your name. I now name you as my heart dictates—Siegmund!"

"Indeed then, fairest of women, I am Siegmund, the Volsung," declares her new-found hero.

"I, too, am of the Volsung race," she responds proudly. "I am Sieglinde, and your true mate."

"Now a new life awaits us!" Siegmund cries, placing his arm about her. Overcome with joy, they rush out into the night.

Wotan has always loved Siegmund and Sieglinde and has closely followed their lives. It was he who struck the sword into the tree. Moreover he knows all that has happened since then. He is now aware that the wrath of Hunding will pursue them.

Wotan firmly believes that these young lovers should mate since they are members of the Volsung race which is half mortal and half god, and, through them, a race of perfect heroes can be founded. Wotan has long tried to create a hero, selfless and unafraid, who might gain possession of the cursed Ring—the Nibelung's Ring. In such hands the Ring would work no harm to the gods. In the meantime the Ring, as Wotan knows, is still in the possession of the giant, Fafner, who has turned himself into a monster dragon and holds it in his forest lair. He has defended it at all times and has even been able to outwit the avaricious schemes of Alberich.

The curtain goes up on the second act revealing a wild and rocky mountain pass. Wotan stands in the foreground, well satisfied with the turn of events. He has summoned his favorite Valkyrie daughter, Brünnhilde, to appear before him for he has work for her to do.

She is a beautiful picture as she dashes in. Her blonde hair is caught under a silver helmet; her shield and spear glitter in the sun, and a red mantle falls from her shoulders disclosing her long white robe. She leaps from Grane, her winged steed, and joyfully makes her way over the rocky path to Wotan's side as she shouts her glorious Valkyrie call: "Ho-yo-to-ho! Ho-yo-to-ho! Hei aha!"

Brünnhilde's Call

Wotan quickly explains everything that has happened to Siegmund and Sieglinde and adds that Hunding is even now on the heels of the lovers. A combat between Hunding and Siegmund is inevitable. The Volsung is armed with the magic sword, Helpneed, but, as an added precaution, Wotan wishes Brünnhilde to be present to protect Siegmund with her shield. Hunding must fall! All this is welcome news to the Valkyrie and she joyfully makes ready to obey.

As she climbs to the higher rocks where her steed is waiting, she catches a glimpse of the pass below. Turning toward Wotan, she warns him humorously:

"Trouble is brewing for you, Father. Here comes Fricka, your wife, storm-clouds of fury on her brow, lashing unmercifully the exhausted rams that draw her chariot. I leave you to your fate! . . . . Ho-yo-to-ho! Ho-yo-to-ho! Hei aha!"

Stormy indeed is Fricka's entrance. She, too, has learned of the flight of the lovers. But Fricka is not concerned with the ultimate fate of Valhalla nor with the creation of a race of perfect heroes. Her concern is for the wrong done to Hunding. She has no patience with Wotan's desire to protect the lovers.

"Here she comes with wrath in her eyes," mutters Wotan to himself, and in a stern voice he asks, "What brings you here?"

"You know full well," says Fricka. "For Hunding's rights I plead."

"But these young lives together shall found a race of heroes whom we need," Wotan tries to explain. "The deep distress that looms before Valhalla demands a man, a hero, who will work for the world's good of his own free will, quite apart from any intervention by the gods."

"And yet I hold the law of convention has been broken by Sieglinde's flight from Hunding's roof," cries Fricka, "and I demand that you withdraw your protection from the lovers!"

Finally, after a long argument, Wotan is forced to yield. Having won her point, Fricka turns to go. As she mounts her ram-drawn chariot, Brünnhilde appears on the rocks above and for a moment she and Fricka gaze at each other with bitter hatred.

"Hasten! The all-wise Father waits for you with new commands," shrills Fricka as she lashes her rams into action. With anxious wonder Brünnhilde hurries to Wotan and finds him in a mood of deep dejection.

"Dearest Father, never have I seen you so worn and grieved," she cries. "What troubles you?"

To her dismay Wotan flings up his arms and cries, "Through me a desperate doom descends upon the gods. Of all creatures that live and breathe, I am the most unhappy."

Much alarmed, Brünnhilde drops spear and shield, flings off her helmet, and sinks at Wotan's feet. She leans against him with child-like confidence and devotion, begging him to tell her all his woe.

Wotan muses a while. Then he begins slowly to confide his inmost thoughts. He tells Brünnhilde the tale of the stolen Rhinegold. How a Nibelung, Alberich, had fashioned from it a magic Ring—the Nibelung's Ring—the full power of which he alone could wield because he had foresworn love for its sake. How Wotan, through trickery, (for he did not spare himself when talking to his beloved daughter) had wrested the ring from Alberich and received the curse of the Nibelung. He describes the warning of Erda, the Earth-mother, to give up the Ring, and his reluctant acquiescence. He tells of the giant Fafner who now owns the Ring and has turned himself into a monster dragon to protect the treasure from the world.

He admits his fear that the gods are doomed. To protect them he has, he says, created the wonderful race of Volsungs. Now the love of these two—Siegmund and Sieglinde—has given him hope that an ideal hero may be born. But Fricka has intervened and has demanded victory for Hunding in the coming combat. Against his desires, against his deepest convictions, Wotan has been compelled to give his word of honor to Fricka that her wishes will be carried out.

At these words he is again consumed with wrath that strikes terror to Brünnhilde's heart.

"What am I, your child, to do? Command me, Father!" she cries.

"Heed not what I at first decreed, but obey Fricka's will," he tells her.

"Surely this cannot be," cries Brünnhilde. "I know your love for Siegmund and because of this great love I must shield the Volsung."

"No," mutters Wotan sternly and sorrowfully. "The victory must go to Hunding. Watch alertly in the coming fray. Siegmund swings a mighty sword."

Brünnhilde is unconvinced. She knows that Wotan is issuing commands contrary to his true desire. This gives her courage to flout him and to say that she intends to disobey him. Wotan fiercely warns her not to awaken his godly anger by disobedience.

"Siegmund must fall!" he says. "You, my child, must work my will!" He turns hastily away while Brünnhilde stands still in stunned amazement. She slowly picks up spear and shield and puts on her helmet. "How heavy these are," she sighs. "I go with foreboding to the fray."

The curtain rising on the third act shows another part of a wild mountain region. Presently Siegmund appears, guiding the faltering steps of Sieglinde who clings to him, exhausted. Gently he makes her comfortable on a grassy knoll where she falls back, utterly spent. Siegmund bends over her anxiously.

Brünnhilde, who has long been watching them from a nearby height, appears before them. She stands erect and her imperious manner gives no hint of the pity she feels for them. She now tells Siegmund that she is to carry him on her winged steed to Valhalla where he is to join the heroic bodyguard of the gods.

The splendors of Valhalla make no impression on Siegmund. "Shall I find my father, the Volsung, there?" he asks. Brünnhilde assures him that he will.

"And now tell me," he begs, "will Sieglinde be there too?"

At this the Valkyrie sadly shakes her head. "Ah, no! She must linger here on earth for a time, alone."

When he hears this, Siegmund turns to kiss Sieglinde and then says that the glory of Valhalla cannot make up for the loss of love. Since Sieglinde cannot be with him there, he will refuse to go.

Brünnhilde tells him sternly that his fate has been decreed by Wotan himself and that he is to die. Siegmund refuses to believe this. He has his powerful sword and is scornful of "puny Hunding's" fighting powers.

"Rash you are!" Brünnhilde now speaks haughtily. "He who gave magic power to your sword has withdrawn it. I tell you again, your doom is sealed!"

At these words Siegmund draws his sword to end Sieglinde's life rather than leave her unprotected and alone. At this sign of his overwhelming love, Brünnhilde's heart relents. She holds back his sword and cries: "Volsung, my brave hero, hear me! Sieglinde shall live and you with her! Even now the hunting horn of Hunding is sounding. He is on your trail. On to the fray! I will protect you!"

It grows dark with storm clouds and a sinister wind hisses across the heights. Thunder resounds through the mountains as lightning flashes reveal Hunding who stands on the heights and sounds his horn. Siegmund, with an exultant cry, rushes to meet his foe, while Sieglinde, terror-stricken, looks on from the pass below.

As they fight Brünnhilde stands behind Siegmund, ready to protect him, and Siegmund appears to have the advantage. When he raises his sword for his mightiest thrust, a crash of thunder louder than any before tears over the heights and before them in a red glow stands Wotan, now a God of Wrath.

With one stroke of his world-governing spear he splinters Siegmund's sword, and Hunding leaps upon his defenceless foe and kills him. With a wild cry of anguish Sieglinde falls senseless. Brünnhilde disappears. One contemptuous glance from Wotan's blazing eyes and Hunding, too, falls dead. Almost at once Brünnhilde is seen rushing toward the senseless form of Sieglinde which she lifts and, half carrying, drags away.

Before the next scene is revealed the orchestra sounds the famous music, magnificent in its wild abandon, which has become a favorite concert piece, *The Ride of the Valkyries.*

The scene of the last act shows a massive rock which fills the center of the stage. This is the favorite meeting place of the Valkyries. One of them is standing on a point of look-out, shielding her eyes for a better sight of her sister Valkyries riding that way. "Ho-yo-to-ho!" she calls, and is answered by each arrival. One after another they clatter in, asking each other gayly, "What dead hero did you capture today?" Each new-

comer is welcomed with their boisterous call. . . . . They now wait
for Brünnhilde.

Siegruna, on the highest peak, suddenly cries jubilantly, "She comes!
She comes! She is riding in mad haste."

"What is hanging from her saddle-bow?" another Valkyrie asks.
"That is no hero!"

Brünnhilde, who is usually so light-hearted, now makes no sound of
greeting. Her sisters watch tensely as she lowers herself from her steed
and makes her way toward them in terrified haste. She is supporting the
unconscious form of Sieglinde. Brünnhilde breathlessly pours out her
story.

"Help me to save this woman, dear Sisters!" But they draw back in
fear, divided between their love for Brünnhilde and their horror at her
disobedience.

"Which one of you will lend me her horse to speed this woman to
safety? My steed is spent!" But one by one they refuse. In the distance
they already hear the thunderous approach of Wotan.

"Where can she go?" Brünnhilde cries, distracted. Sieglinde opens her
eyes and looks about her, bewildered.

"To the eastward lies a tangled forest," one of her sisters ventures.
"In its depths dread Fafner has his lair, guarding the golden treasure.
Wotan shuns that forest. Let the woman flee there."

Brünnhilde explains this to Sieglinde while pressing into her hands
the fragments of Siegmund's sword which she bids her guard with great
care. "One day you will bear a son whose name shall be Siegfried.
Remember that! This sword will be a magic weapon for him. Brave all
danger for your son's sake!" At these words Sieglinde staggers away.

Wotan now appears and strides fiercely toward them. The sisters
crowd about Brünnhilde. They plead for her and try to shield her from
his wrath, but the god angrily silences them.

"You are a soft-hearted brood! Have I so little steeled you against
distress? How you whimper! Brünnhilde has defied me! She must be
punished!"

The Valkyries stir in terror, but Brünnhilde steps forth slowly and
speaks calmly: "Here I am, Father. Name my punishment!"

Wotan answers, "Nay, I do not punish. You yourself have wrought
your woe. No longer shall you be a proud Valkyrie bringing valiant
heroes to Valhalla's halls. Broken are the bonds that bound you to me.
You are banished forever from the realm of the gods!"

With loud lamenting the Valkyries cry, "Oh Sister . . . . what woe."

Brünnhilde, stunned, beseeches him, "Father, you cannot mean this!"
But Wotan answers sadly, "What I have spoken must hold. Your
doom is fixed."

Once more, the agonized voices of Brünnhilde's sisters rise in pleading:
"Oh Father! Stay your words!"

"Did you not hear me?" Wotan thunders. "Never again shall
Brünnhilde ride out the storm in your gallant company. She is no
longer of the god-like brood. Henceforth as helpless mortal woman she
must obey any mortal man who wins her."

Brünnhilde, wailing, sinks upon the ground. The rest recoil and then
slowly mount their waiting steeds and ride away. For a long time
Brünnhilde lies prostrate. At last she speaks. "Father, your own decree
I carried out!"

"That decree I had reversed," Wotan retorts angrily.

"I knew that was against your inmost heart's desire," she answers
proudly. "Your true will, which I have ever been, was bound to aid
the Volsung whom you loved. Therefore did I thwart your harsh
command."

Half relenting, Wotan speaks. "Yes, what you did I longed to do,
but bound by law I had to hide the torture of my heart." Brünnhilde
is stirred by his words. "You, my child," he continues, "were ever the
reflection of my own true self, but henceforth we can no longer be
together. Never again will you behold my face!"

Brünnhilde draws closer at his broken words and lays her head upon
his knee. "Then, beloved Father, if I am cast off, shame not yourself by
bringing shame to me. See that I, a defenceless woman, fall not into the
hands of a coward. Guard me from such a fate!"

Wotan is deeply moved. He strokes the Valkyrie's golden hair and
muses silently. At last he speaks. "Here on this rock you will be cast into
a deep sleep, and girdled by a ring of seething flames. This fiery menace
will keep away all craven hearts. Only a perfect hero, unafraid, will
brave the ring of fire to reach your side."

With infinite relief and gratitude Brünnhilde gazes into Wotan's eyes
as he clasps her to him in a long embrace.

Wotan's Last Words to the Valkyrie

very slowly

So kiss I your god —— head a - way

When Brünnhilde sinks into magic sleep, Wotan tenderly carries her to what is henceforth known as "Brünnhilde's Rock". He lays her down gently and places her helmet partly over her face. He then places her shield upon her breast and her spear at her side. He gazes at her silently for a long time and then turns to call upon Loki, the Fire God.

Loki! Loki!
Hear me and heed!
As I found you first
In a fiery glow,
Speed now to me—
In another.

Capricious you were
But I bound you fast.
Now kindle your fire
For my own desire.
Loki! Loki!
Come hither with speed!

As the words die upon his lips, great Wotan strikes his spear three times into the quivering earth. A spurt of flame darts upward, then another, and another. The music of the flames mingles with the melody of Wotan's last decree: "He whose spirit fears my world-governing spear will never dare to brave this fiery height."

Flame Music

With markings of his spear the god extends the fiery course. The ring of flames complete, he turns to go but pauses again and again for one more look at the sleeping maiden. At last, with heavy heart, he turns once more, then slowly disappears.

The leaping flames still flicker in the thickening gloom. The music dies down gradually. The brave Valkyrie sleeps, silent, alone on her mountain top.

SIEGFRIED

or
THE
HERO and THE DRAGON
by RICHARD WAGNER

(Third Opera of The Nibelung's Ring)

Siegfried

SIEGFRIED, the hero of this story, has lived a rugged life in the wilds of a forest and is handsome and strong and brave. Having no kin of his own, he has been reared by an ugly, uncouth dwarf named Mime, an aged, shambling creature, one of the race of Nibelungs who prefer to dwell in dark caves away from the light of day. In spite of all Mime's care, Siegfried detests his guardian. He knows instinctively—though there has been no one to tell him so—that Mime is a wily schemer and not to be trusted.

Yet Mime's cavern in the depths of the forest is the only spot Siegfried can call "home". His steps invariably turn in that direction and lead him back, no matter how weary he is, or how far he may have wandered. Siegfried knows nothing of himself—not even his own name, or who his parents were, or how he came to live in this lonely forest. Again and again he questions Mime eagerly, only to be put off by explanations which he knows to be fantastic and untrue.

The boy, now grown to young manhood, is lonely and unhappy. Why, he often asks himself, is he the only living creature in the whole forest without a companion of his own kind? Why is there no one for him? . . . . The wild beasts are his only friends. They welcome him as they would a strange, young cub, and play with him because he seems almost one of them. He knows no fear, nor does he wish to harm any living creature—except, perhaps, evil-hearted Mime.

It is strange that he detests the dwarf for he is the only human being Siegfried has ever known. Surely he cannot be related to him, Siegfried thinks, for he has often seen his own image in pools of still water and he cannot see that he has any resemblance to the ugly dwarf! Siegfried has repeatedly begged Mime to explain all these things which trouble him.

"Why is there no young thing in the forest like myself? . . . Why have I no companion, no playmate of my own kind? . . . . Who am I, anyway? . . . . Who was my mother . . . . my father? . . . . How did I come here? . . . . Where did I come from?"

To all this Mime invariably replies, "I am your father. I brought you up, an infant in my arms . . . ."

His clumsy attempts to deceive always send Siegfried into a towering rage for he knows that Mime is lying to him. He invariably ends by telling the dwarf that he detests the very sight of him and then storms out into the forest to work off his temper and regain his self-control.

The first scene of *Siegfried* shows a yawning cavern, inside of which is a great forge. Nearby lie huge bellows for fanning the flame while tools are scattered about in every direction. The long-bearded dwarf, Mime, sits hunched up at the anvil. His thoughts are gloomy as he busily rains blows on the hot tempered steel out of which he is making a sword. Although he does not speak, the orchestra plays descriptive themes which tell much of what he is thinking.

Long ages ago Mime had pursued his craft as a smith in the dismal realm of the Nibelungs where he toiled for his cruel brother, Alberich. After Alberich brought to Nibelheim the Rhinegold which he stole from the Rhine-maidens, Mime had fashioned part of it into a magic Helmet. The power of this Helmet could make its wearer invisible, or transport him to the ends of the earth in less than a minute; or turn him into any kind of creature, large or small. Mime hoped to keep this Helmet, but Alberich discovered it and took it for himself, giving Mime only kicks and blows as reward for his skillful labor.

Mime had been present when the Ring had been made for Alberich— that Ring of strange power which was to have made his brother Nibelung master of the world. Mime now thinks of all that has happened to the Ring since then. How the god Wotan had forcibly taken it from Alberich. How his brother had then cursed it so that it would bring sorrow and death to anyone who wore it. How Wotan had given it and the gold gained through its power to the giants, Fasolt and Fafner. How then the curse had worked its evil—Fafner had killed his brother over a division of the treasure, and now lay hidden in a dark cavern. How he had used the magic Helmet to turn himself into a terrible dragon to guard his gold and his Ring.

Mime had always planned to get the Ring for himself, and thereby achieve supreme power, but he was too much of a coward to attempt to fight the dragon. For a long time he had not known what to do. Then good fortune had left an infant in his care and Mime knew that this child was Siegfried.

He had carefully reared the boy to young manhood. But he had done this only because he wanted Siegfried to slay the dragon. This accomplished, Mime felt sure that he could find some way to rid himself of his charge. With all obstacles removed, he would then get the gold, the Ring, and the magic Helmet all in his own hands! Whenever he thought of it he chuckled with malicious glee!

To equip Siegfried to fight the dragon, Mime had been trying to forge a good sword. Although the dwarf considered himself a master craftsman and liked to boast about it, too, he had not yet succeeded in forging a blade which Siegfried could not splinter at a blow. This had happened so often that Mime was growing more and more discouraged.

These were his thoughts as he sat at the anvil.

Mime ceases his work and carefully examines the blade in his hands. "This sword," he says, "should be strong enough to serve a giant. Yet in the hands of that hot-headed stripling it will probably be broken into bits, like a mere toy!"

He drops his tools, scratches his head, and heaves a long sigh. "There is only one sword that can defy his strength," Mime acknowledges grimly, "but that sword I cannot weld. The pieces will not hold together, try as I will." He glances sorrowfully at the ground where the fragments of an ancient sword are lying. Then he gives a start, for Siegfried's horn is heard in the distance.

Siegfried's Horn

A few minutes later Siegfried storms in, leading a bear cub on a leash. He playfully drives the animal toward Mime, cordially inviting him to eat the dwarf. Terror-stricken, Mime crouches down behind the anvil while the youth roars with delight. At last, having tired of teasing, Siegfried asks to see the latest example of the sword-maker's skill, but Mime refuses to leave his hiding place until the bear is sent away. This done, he comes out, and with many self-compliments, hands the latest sword to Siegfried.

As usual, Siegfried makes short work of it. A single blow on the anvil and the blade is splintered. Disappointed again, Siegfried throttles Mime until the little fellow cries for mercy. He then throws himself sullenly on a bench with his back to the dwarf.

Mime tries to please him by bringing food and drink, but the young man pushes it away impatiently. Siegfried, musing, asks himself again a question which has long perplexed him. Why, since he feels such an honest loathing for Mime, does he continue to return to this "home" when he can easily care for himself. Suddenly he has an inspiration. The answer must be that Mime is the only person who knows all about him, who can tell him who he really is!

Siegfried springs up. He takes hold of Mime and tells him that he will *shake* the truth out of him this time.

Mime quakes with fright and cries, "Let loose! Let me go! I will tell you all you ask, you ungrateful wretch!" He seats himself close to Siegfried and begins.

"I am no father and no kin of yours," he says, "and yet to me you owe your very life." He pauses, but Siegfried prods him impatiently.

"Go on! Go on!" he cries.

Mime continues. "One day a woman came into my workshop in the forest seeking shelter from the storm. For months she had wandered, ill and weak. I took her in and there her child was born. You were this child. Before the end she murmured, 'I am Sieglinde,' and with her dying breath she gave you the name 'Siegfried'!"

"And so for me my mother gave her life." Siegfried's words come slowly, for he is deeply moved. "And my father?" Again his voice is eager.

"I knew him not," says Mime. "Your mother said he had been slain in combat."

"How do I know you are telling me the truth?" cries Siegfried, his old suspicions rising. "What proof have you?"

"The proof lies here," says Mime. He stoops and gathers up the pieces of the old sword, placing them in Siegfried's hands as the youth looks on in wonder. "Your mother said, 'This is a treasure. Guard it for the child. It was his father's sword!'"

Siegfried now examines the fragments proudly. Then, springing up, he declares, "You must forge me a blade from these. It will be the weapon I have longed for. Cheat me not again with toy swords, but prove you are the master smith you say you are!"

At these words Mime shows great alarm, holding up his hands in trembling supplication, but Siegfried fails to notice him. "When the sword is done, I will wander forth into the world," he continues happily. "You are not my father nor any kin to me. Far from here I will seek another home and never again return to this hearth!" With the last words he is out of the cave and away to the sunlit forest.

In desperation Mime calls after him, "Stay! Siegfried! Stay!", but the wind whistling through the trees is Mime's only answer. It sounds for all the world like mocking laughter, Mime thinks—the way Siegfried so often laughs at him. . . . Mime shivers with a strange foreboding.

The dwarf is indeed in a dilemma. For all his boasting, the Nibelung knows he cannot mend this magic sword which Siegmund carried to his last and fatal combat and which was shattered by the world-governing spear of Wotan, chief of all the gods. Who can mend it, since it defies even Mime's skill?

Mime knows the entire history of this sword called Helpneed but he does not know who can weld the broken bits into a new blade. To complete Mime's plans Siegfried must have a proper weapon. The aged dwarf has not reared his charge from infancy out of love for him, but has planned to use him to do away with the dragon guarding the Nibelung's Ring.

Again Mime begins to day-dream but this time his nodding head jerks back alertly as he perceives a stranger standing in the entrance to the cavern. Mime barely grunts a welcome, and is a most ungracious host because he is eager to get at his sword-making, discouraging as it is. He knows only too well what will happen if Siegfried returns to find the weapon unfinished. But his mysterious visitor calmly enters and seats himself without invitation. He then engages Mime in conversation. After a time they make a wager, each agreeing to sacrifice his head if he cannot answer any three questions the other may ask.

Mime puts his questions first. He considers all of them so difficult that he is very confident. To his amazement they are quickly answered. Then it is the stranger's turn to ask three questions. Mime is able to solve the first two with ease and his courage rises. But the third question is the very one Mime cannot answer!

"Whose hand," demands the stranger, "will mend the sword of Siegmund—the sword called Helpneed?"

Mime shakes his head helplessly. Had he, a master-smith, not tried to weld it and failed miserably?

"Then I will tell you," announces the stranger rising. As his spear point touches the ground a low rumble of thunder is heard and sparks seem to flash from his eyes. Mime looks up, terror-stricken, and is overcome with awe and amazement when he recognizes his visitor as Wotan himself. The words the god speaks are full of portent. "Only one who is *without fear* can weld the fragments into a perfect blade," he says. "Heed what I have told you!" Wotan turns away. "As for your stupid head which you have forfeited," he calls back, "I leave it to fall into better hands than mine." Without another word he disappears.

Scarcely has he gone when Siegfried returns. He abuses Mime more cruelly than usual when he finds the sword still in fragments.

"I will do it myself!" he shouts, and with confident ease (since he is without fear) he forges a perfect blade, singing lustily as he does so.

Sword Song

The sword finished, Siegfried swings the burnished blade on high and jubilantly announces that he must set out at once in search of new adventures. He remembers the fierce dragon Mime has described to him so often and now decides to go after him. First, however, to test the sword, he tries it on the anvil. A single blow, and the anvil breaks in two!

As the curtain rises on the second act it reveals the forest jungle near the dragon's lair. The music stirs and throbs with growling foreboding. In the gloom a figure crouches. It is Alberich, the Nibelung, whose Ring the dragon holds. Alberich, jealous of his lost power, haunts the spot, though he is helpless to regain his treasure.

His night vigil has been tedious. "Is this the dawn?" he mutters as he notices a faint glow, and a fitful gust of wind breaks the night's calm. "Who comes there, shining in the shadow?" he asks as the glow brightens. In another moment he recognizes his ancient enemy, Wotan.

The Nibelung recoils in dread. "What are you doing here, you shameless thief?" he growls.

"Why bide you here by Fafner's cave?" demands Wotan mildly. "I come to observe. Not to act!"

"You arch-conspirator!" Alberich bursts out spitefully. "If I were now as stupid as I once was, you would again cheat me out of the Ring if I had it. Well I know your tricks."

Although Wotan draws himself up haughtily Alberich continues. "How proud are your threats of menacing power. Yet should this

Nibelung once more grasp the Ring, then even you would tremble, you high protector of heroes! It is fear of this that sinks your spirit and tears you with endless care!"

"Your intentions I know full well," replies Wotan quietly. "Wrangle with your brother, Mime, who even now is leading a young hero on this path to kill the dragon. The youth knows nothing of the Ring or of the treasure."

"And I need fight only Mime for the Ring?" asks Alberich, scarcely able to believe what he has heard.

"It is so decreed," declares Wotan. "Fafner will be killed. Then two Nibelungs will fight. I wish the winner luck!"

"And you speak truly?" Alberich asks in wild anticipation.

"I do. So why not warn Fafner of his fate?" suggests Wotan. "Mayhap you can bargain with him."

Alberich, alert to his own advantage, now cries out to the dragon, "Fafner, beware! A swordsman comes to end your life. Give me the Ring and I will leave you all the gold and see that you come to no harm."

But Fafner growls, "I yearn for a new victim. As for the Ring, I own it and here it remains. Let me sleep."

"Aha! Alberich! That shot failed," says Wotan, laughing at his foe's discomfiture. "Whatever else may happen here, you shall see." With these words the god disappears and a gust of wind stirs the leaves as if at the passing of a ghost. Alberich silently resumes his vigil.

As the dawn breaks, Mime and Siegfried approach the spot. Alberich, hidden in a cleft of the rocks, watches them. Mime carefully takes in the scene. "Here we are," he says, looking about him.

Siegfried nonchalantly seats himself under a tree. "All night we have wandered," he observes. "So this is the place where I am to learn fear?"

Mime seats himself opposite, keeping the entrance to the dragon's lair well in sight so that he can flee at the least hint of danger. He proceeds, now, to give Siegfried a detailed description of the monster.

"Trust me, you fearless one," Mime says. "You will learn to tremble here. A monstrous maw has the brute. He will swallow you whole!"

"To baffle him, I will refuse to thrust myself down his throat," answers Siegfried lightly.

"He who is seared by his fiery breath will shrivel and die," warns Mime.

"Then will I leap lightly aside to escape his venom," is Siegfried's response.

"His twisting tail will crush you in its toils!" As Mime says this he can scarcely keep a note of satisfaction from his voice.

"Then will I keep a wary eye on his movements," replies Siegfried calmly. "But, tell me, has the brute a heart?"

"A cruel and hardened heart!" cries Mime.

"His heart lies where lies the heart of man and beast?" persists Siegfried.

"No doubt it does," says Mime, wondering.

"Then I will straightway plunge my sword into his heart!" Siegfried speaks with confidence.

"I will leave you now," announces Mime, eager to be at a safe distance. When he is out of ear-shot he mutters, "Fafner and Siegfried—Siegfried and Fafner . . . . I wish they would kill each other!"

Siegfried, left alone, stretches out under a tree, and for a time nothing is heard but the soft murmur of rustling leaves and the twittering of birds. This forest music is often played as a concert piece and is familiar to many who do not know the complete opera.

Forest Murmurs

Presently the young hero is attracted by the song of a bird in the tree over his head. Looking up, he says, "If I could only understand what that bird is singing perhaps it would tell me something I should know." His eyes light on a clump of reeds nearby, and, jumping up, he whittles himself a kind of whistle. With this new toy he tries to imitate the bird's song, but without success. Siegfried shakes his head with vexation.

"This will never do," he says. Then he addresses the bird, "Here, I will sing you another tune," and he sounds a merry call on his horn.

There is a stir in the underbrush and the terrible head and forepaws of the dragon appear as he crawls out of his lair. Siegfried turns, and then springs up and laughs.

"Here I was singing a love song to the bird. What a sweet companion my song has brought me!"

Fafner, the dragon, pauses at sight of Siegfried. "Who are you?" he asks.

"Oho! shouts Siegfried. "Are you a beast that has speech? Can you teach me fear?"

"You are over-bold, I am thinking," growls the dragon. "I came for water and a precious morsel of food I find in my path." At these grim words he opens his immense jaws and lashes his tail in fury. "Come on, you brawler," he roars.

The contest now begins. The advantage is apparently on the dragon's side, but Siegfried fights valiantly and does not lose his head. In fact he even laughs at the unwieldly movements of his bulky opponent. The huge tail lashes out with venomous fury but Siegfried nimbly escapes the toils. As the monster lunges toward him the young swordsman deftly leaps to one side, watches his chance, and plunges his sword straight into the dragon's heart!

Fafner rolls over, dying. In a weak voice he gasps, "Who are you, stalwart youth, who feared me not, and whose sword has struck my heart? I know your brain did not devise this murderous deed."

"Little do I know of myself," replies Siegfried, "not even who I am. But I know this—'twas you yourself incited me to kill you."

"Would you then know whom you have done to death?" demands Fafner. "Listen to what I tell you." Gathering his failing strength, Fafner continues:

"The giants, Fasolt and Fafner, of a strong and generous race, once ruled on earth. Fasolt, my brother, received his death blow from me when we fought over the cursed gold the gods had given us. Then I turned myself into a monster. Here I have guarded the treasure ever since, and now I die." Fafner pauses for a moment while Siegfried remains speechless with amazement. Then Fafner begins again: "Now heed this warning. Treachery surrounds this gold and brings danger to its possessor. He who led you here even now plots your end. Be on your guard!"

Siegfried is too startled at this revelation to speak, but at last he stammers, "Wierd monster, I am almost sorry I have killed you. You know so much! Perchance you can tell me of my parents. My name is Siegfried. Will that help?"

"Siegfried!" Fafner repeats the name in wonder. He vainly strives to speak, then heaves a great sigh and dies.

Siegfried stands motionless. At last he draws his splendid sword from Fafner's heart. As he does this the dragon's blood, spurting on his hand, seems to sting his flesh. He puts his hand instinctively to his lips and finds that the blood tastes bitter, but he forgets this in the miracle of the next moment. He suddenly realizes that he can understand the song of the bird. He listens intently to the words.

"Ho, Siegfried, the precious gold lies in yonder cave, and with it lies the magic Helmet which can serve you well. And there is also that rarest treasure, the Nibelung's Ring. He who wears it can become master of the world!"

"Thank you, little bird. Henceforth I will follow your voice," Siegfried responds, and he boldly enters the yawning cavern which has been the dragon's lair.

Scarcely has Siegfried disappeared when Mime slinks into view, timidly assuring himself that Fafner is actually dead. At the same time Alberich comes out from his hiding-place to watch his brother Nibelung. When he does not find Siegfried anywhere, Mime steals toward the cavern, but Alberich darts ahead of him and bars the way.

"Where are you slinking to, you sly and slippery rogue?" he cries.

"Accursed brother, what brings you here?" Mime retorts, furiously.

"Are you thirsting for my gold?" snarls Alberich.

"The gold is mine!" cries Mime. "I have won it by toil and pain. It shall not escape me now!" As Mime says this, he attempts to push Alberich aside.

"Yours!" cries Alberich who is now mad with fury. "Was it you who stole the gold from the depths of the Rhine and made the Ring?"

"I fashioned the magic Helmet," Mime reminds him proudly, "which can make its wearer invisible or, in a trice, can change him to another shape."

"You fool! What could you ever have done without the power of my Ring behind you?" sneers his brother Nibelung.

"Your Ring!" mocks Mime. "Where is it now? What you have lost, my craftiness shall win for me!"

"A shining hero is now lord over the Ring," hisses Alberich.

"I brought him up." Mime speaks eagerly. "For all my toil he must repay me." Then Mime's scheming mind conceives a new plan. With pretended humility he suggests that Alberich take the Ring if he, Mime, can have the magic Helmet. But Alberich receives this idea with mocking scorn.

"I hold the Ring and you the Helmet? Then never could I rest from your dastardly plotting!"

They are still wrangling when Siegfried steps out of the cave. The Helmet is dangling from his belt, the Ring is on his finger. Mime and

Alberich hide, but watch Siegfried as he examines both objects. "What these baubles may be worth to me I do not know," he says. "I have taken them only because my bird counselor told me to." Siegfried has left the gold untouched, for it means nothing to him.

The bird now speaks again to the young hero and tells him of Mime's plan to kill him with a cup of poisoned broth in order to gain the treasure for himself. When Mime appears with mincing steps and proffers the poisoned brew with sly, deceptive words of friendliness, Siegfried brusquely refuses. Further conversation follows during which Mime unconsciously reveals his hatred of Siegfried and his secret ambitions. He becomes fiercely insistent when Siegfried refuses the cup a second time.

"Hey! Just try it. Trust to my skill!" but his malicious chuckle betrays him. Unable longer to control his loathing for the dwarf, Siegfried draws his sword and slays him. He throws the body into the cave, saying, "Lie there beside your coveted treasure."

Tired from his task, Siegfried now throws himself under a tree to rest. For a long time nothing can be heard but the soft murmuring sounds of the forest. Once again the bird begins to sing. This time Siegfried listens with growing wonder and surprise.

The Wood-bird's Song

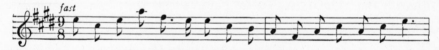

Ho, Siegfried, Hero, Listen!
A glorious maid lies sleeping
On a distant mountain-top.
Only a hero may break through the fire
That encircles Brünnhilde's Rock.

"How can I find this maid?" Siegfried asks joyfully.

"Only a hero *to whom fear is unknown* can reach Brünnhilde," the bird tells him. "For such a one the maiden waits."

At these words Siegfried springs up crying, "The stupid one who never learned to fear—surely that is myself! Oh bird, lead the way! Show me the path to Brünnhilde's Rock!"

When the curtain rises on the last act, the scene is a wild region at the base of a steep mountain side. It is night. Wotan, seated on a rock, is waiting for Siegfried whose path leads this way. The chief of the gods knows that the young hero has killed the dragon, but intends to give his fearlessness a final test.

With the first streak of dawn Siegfried appears. He is dashing along when suddenly he stops in his tracks, looking first to the right and then to the left. "I have lost my bird pilot," he exclaims. "Now where am I?"

"Whither would you go?" Wotan's voice startles Siegfried who has not seen him.

"I would find a rock encircled by fire on which sleeps a beautiful maid!" explains Siegfried eagerly. "Can you show me the way?"

Wotan does not answer this question at once. He finds comfort in this meeting with the perfect hero and leads him on to talk. Siegfried gives him a naïve description of the dragon and then goes on to tell of the wood-bird's song and how he came to forge the sword he carries. But at last the youth grows impatient.

"Tell me, old man, the way up the mountain. Or, if you know it not, stand aside, but hold me here no longer!"

Wotan draws himself up and strikes the point of his spear into the ground. A low rumble of thunder is heard. High above them the ring of fire glows brightly. "Behold the raging furnace awaiting you," warns Wotan. "Away, foolhardy youth!"

"Stand back!" shouts Siegfried. "I shall go straight through the flames!" But as he starts forward impetuously, Wotan stretches out his spear and bars his path.

"If you fear not the fire, then fear my spear," he commands. "The sword you hold was once shattered against this shaft. Now again this immortal spear will break it!"

Siegfried fiercely draws his sword. "Hah! Then I am at last facing my father's foe! Now for revenge! Stretch out your mighty spear and let me shatter it!" The combat that follows is brief with Siegfried victor.

Wotan recoils, a fragment of his spear still in his hand. "Proceed," he says in muffled tones. "I cannot hold you back!"

Siegfried dashes forward with an exultant cry and leaps into the flames. Wotan watches silently, then turns away and vanishes forever from the sight of man.

As Siegfried climbs on and on his horn sounds clearly. When he finally rounds the mountain top the fiery glow dies down and fades into thin mist. As this clears the peak is seen in bright sunshine with blue skies above. In the foreground is Brünnhilde's Rock. Siegfried appears at the back and looks about with pleased surprise.

"What a peaceful spot is this sunny height," he says. Then, peering through the trees, he adds, "But what lies there, a horse?" He is filled with wonder for he does not know that this is Brünnhilde's faithful steed held fast in sleep by the same magic spell that binds his mistress. Siegfried then discovers the sleeping form underneath a great pine tree. Slowly he draws near and, lifting the shield, sees Brünnhilde's face partly concealed by the helmet.

"A young warrior," he says. "How handsome is his face!" He looks at the "warrior" anxiously. "But he breathes heavily. I will loosen his armor."

With great care Siegfried cuts through the rings of steel and also removes the helmet. Then he starts back with an expression of dismay which gradually changes to awed admiration. Brünnhilde lies before him. She is clothed in soft flowing garments and her long hair shines in the sun.

"This is no man!" he cries, staggering backward. "How can I waken her . . . . I am trembling . . . . Can this, at last, be fear?" he asks himself. Finally he summons courage and bends down to kiss her.

As he does so Brünnhilde opens her eyes. For some moments they gaze at each other in silent wonder. Then Brünnhilde, stretching forth her arms, salutes the day.

"O Sun, all hail!"

"All hail to her who gave me life," responds Siegfried, "that I have lived to see this blessed day!"

"All hail to her," repeats Brünnhilde. "It is for you I have awakened."

Siegfried, who has drawn back, now advances toward her. Brünnhilde, who has risen, looks about her and then gazes upon her deliverer with rapture. Their hearts are filled with happiness and they embrace.

These two have found each other as fate long ago decreed. Now, in a transport of joy, they sing their song of love.

Love Duet

DIE
GÖTTERDÄMMERUNG
or
THE
TWILIGHT of THE GODS
by RICHARD WAGNER

(Fourth Opera of The Nibelung's Ring)

Die Götterdämmerung

THE twilight of the gods had long been foretold. Their glory and might had been built on high-mindedness and justice and fair-dealing. So long as they held to these ideals, they reigned supreme. Wotan, for ages past chief of all the gods, gained his high estate because of his great wisdom. To win this, however, he had compromised with fate. In his youth he had committed the sin of drinking from the Forbidden Spring whose waters came from the source of all knowledge. In this way he had gained the wisdom he coveted, but for it he had been forced to sacrifice the sight of one eye. In arrogance and pride, he had then torn a branch from the World Ash Tree growing near the spring. From this he had carved a shaft for his spear with which he henceforth governed the world.

Wotan, well beloved by those he loved, was thought to be wholly noble. Yet he had lost half of his integrity with the loss of one eye and it was difficult for him to see the right at all times. As a result of this he had marked his reign by broken promises and forgotten treaties, even though he knew that, by so doing, he hastened the twilight of the gods.

Wotan ordered the stronghold, Valhalla, to be built as a symbol of his power and created a race of War-maidens—the Valkyries. It was their duty to fly through the air on winged steeds and pick up warriors who had fallen in battle in order to bring them to Valhalla to form an heroic body-guard for the gods. Wotan did not yet feel secure, however, and he created the noble race of Volsungs, mortals with a god-like strain. From this race the perfect hero, Siegfried, son of Siegmund and Sieglinde, was born. He represents the new order—the spirit of right that is ultimately to rule the world. With the coming of the perfect hero, it has been decreed that the reign of the gods will end.

Therefore, when Wotan met Siegfried at the foot of Brünnhilde's Mountain, the scene was one of great portent. Siegfried carried the sword Helpneed, which, unknown to him, had come from Valhalla and which, in the hands of one without fear, became an unconquerable weapon.

Siegfried, the fearless hero, was thus able to shatter the world-governing spear of Wotan.

With this act the doom of the gods was sealed and Wotan retired from the world to Valhalla to await the end. He ordered the ancient World Ash Tree which had fallen into decay, to be hacked down and hewn into faggots. These, piled high about Valhalla, will one day, at the appointed time, form a funeral pyre for the gods.

All this is told by the Fates in the first scene of *Die Götterdämmerung*. Soft, undulating music is played by the orchestra as the curtain slowly rises.

It is night and the darkest hour just before dawn. The three figures of the Fates clothed in gray robes can be seen dimly in the gloom. Seated on a rocky eminence they spin their endless golden thread of circumstance and speak of Wotan and his adventures . . . . of Alberich and the Nibelung's Ring and many other happenings of the past; but when they try to peer into the future, the golden thread breaks! The Fates cry out in wild surprise and sink slowly into the earth. Their work is done.

As the day dawns and the first rays of the morning sun cast their roseate hue upon the scene, the orchestra sounds this bold theme:

The Siegfried Theme

Then follows other music, soft and tender

The Brünnhilde Theme

In the glory of the early morning Siegfried and Brünnhilde come forth from their rock-bound home on the mountain-top. Siegfried has won Brünnhilde for his wife by dashing through the ring of fire to the rock where she had been held in magic sleep. And Brünnhilde, who was once a War-maiden, Wotan's best loved Valkyrie, is now a mortal woman, content and happy with her lot.

United to Siegfried she has taught him much of the knowledge she remembers from the time when she was a goddess. She has also used her power to render him immune to attack. Knowing, however, that a hero will always face his foe, she has left his back vulnerable. Siegfried is in full armor and is eager to start on new adventures. As pledge of his faithfulness he gives his beloved Brünnhilde the fateful Nibelung's Ring which he had taken from the dragon's lair. He is not interested in the power of the Ring and he is unaware of its curse. Brünnhilde accepts the gift joyfully and in return gives him her shield and her horse, Grane, now no longer a winged steed, but still a charger more wonderful than man has ever mounted.

Their farewell is long and tender. Then Siegfried rides away, merrily sounding his horn.

Siegfried's Horn

He is armed with the good sword, Helpneed, and he wears at his belt the magic Helmet that he also found in the dragon's cave. He thinks it merely a useless bauble. Left alone on her mountain top, Brünnhilde wistfully turns the ring on her finger and dreams of her love. Siegfried's horn sounds fainter and fainter in the distance until at last it dies away. As the curtain goes down the orchestra takes up the story of Siegfried's journey along the Rhine, for this is the direction he has taken. The melodious music is full of life and hope and eagerness, with an underlying movement which recalls the steadily flowing waters of the great river.

Siegfried's Journey

This musical interlude indicates a considerable lapse of time. Then a new mood creeps into the music which continues without pause until the curtain rises on what is designated by the composer as the first act. All that has gone before is considered the *Prelude*.

The new scene, foretold by the music, shows the lordly castle of the Gibichungs on the Rhine. Here young King Gunther reigns, as his father has reigned before him. At the back of the great hall of state high open arches reveal the rolling land extending to the banks of the river. Inside the hall, Gunther is seated on his throne and his fair sister, Gutrune, is by his side. Below and before them is a table set with brimming flagons where black-bearded Hagen, elder half-brother to the King, lolls in insolent ease.

Hagen is the offspring of Gunther's mother and Alberich, the Nibelung. Through his father Hagen is well versed in the history of the Ring which can make its owner master of the world. Hagen knows, too, that Alberich lost the ring to Wotan, that he in turn was forced to give it to the giants and that it has come at last into the possession of Siegfried. It is Hagen's secret ambition to obtain the Ring for himself by any means. Good-natured Gunther and his trusting sister, Gutrune, have many times been innocent tools in the wily hands of this artful schemer. Hagen now has another evil plan. He therefore brings their talk around to the future of their house.

He bewails the fact that the young King is still unwed and that Gutrune is without a husband. To excite Gunther's interest, he tells him that he knows of a beautiful maiden, one altogether worthy to be the bride of a Gibichung. Hagen then describes Brünnhilde and the ring of fire that surrounds her as she sleeps on the mountain top. He does not know that Brünnhilde has already been won by Siegfried but he does know that only a hero utterly without fear can penetrate those flames unharmed.

"Surely my courage is equal to that task," says Gunther.

"That is reserved for one stouter of heart even than you," Hagen tells him.

"Who might be this bravest one?" asks Gunther, somewhat miffed by Hagen's reply.

"Siegfried, the Volsung," Hagen answers. "He is the noblest of heroes, worthy even to be Gutrune's mate!" Hagen slyly enjoys the effect of his words.

"What deed brought him such fame?" asks Gutrune, shyly. Hagen tells her that Siegfried has killed the dragon and, by this deed, has won for himself the famous gold, the magic Helmet and the Nibelung's Ring.

"I have heard of that treasure and the Ring," muses Gunther. "But why should he be interested in winning a bride for me?"

"If he came here and learned to love our beautiful Gutrune, would she not be a worthy reward for such a deed?" Hagen suggests slyly.

"You are but making sport of us, you wicked Hagen," says Gutrune, half playfully, but she cannot let the subject rest. "How could I hope to attract such a hero?"

"Mind you, in yonder chest is stored a charmed potion," Hagen says. "Place your trust in that! Should Siegfried come and so much as taste the magic draught, he will be bound to you forever!" Before speaking further he looks intently at them both. Then he says, "What think you of my plan?"

Although Gunther and Gutrune are honorable and fair-minded, Hagen wins them in the end and they agree to join him in the plot against Siegfried. They are not at all sure, however, that the hero will visit them.

"He will come this way in his wanderings, never fear," Hagen assures them. "Great is the fame of the Gibichungs!"

While they are still in deep discussion, the sound of a horn is heard. Hagen goes to the back of the hall and gazes toward the river. "I see a small boat carrying a warrior and a horse!" he calls.

"Is it coming this way?" cries Gunther.

Hagen does not answer, but puts his hands to his mouth and shouts, "Hoiho! Where are you bound, my merry knight?"

"I am seeking the scion of the Gibichungs," replies a voice from the distance.

"Then behold your goal, ... Siegfried!" cries Hagen, certain that he has guessed who the stranger knight is. Gunther has by this time joined Hagen and they go toward the river to make the stranger welcome.

"Which of you is Gibichung's son?" demands Siegfried. Gunther steps forward. "I am he whom you seek."

"Your fame has reached beyond the Rhine," Siegfried says. "So fight me now, or be my friend."

"No enemy is here," Gunther assures him. "You are as welcome as a brother."

During this exchange of greetings Siegfried has been leaning against his horse, Grane. Now he asks, "Where can I stable my steed?"

"I will take him in charge," offers Hagen. Siegfried looks at him questioningly.

"You called me by name," he says, "and yet, are we not strangers?"

"Your mighty strength and build revealed you," explains Hagen as he leads the steed away.

Gunther and Siegfried enter the hall. Gutrune has disappeared and the young King turns to Siegfried, saying, "Welcome, O hero, to these ancient halls where dwelt my fathers. Look upon this kingdom as your own. I offer you my lands, my vassals and myself."

"No lands or vassals have I," says Siegfried. "Only the strength of my right arm can I offer you, and this noble sword, my only weapon."

Hagen stands behind them, listening intently. Now he croaks: "But you are hailed as lord of the Nibelung's treasure."

"Oh, that treasure!" Siegfried scoffs. "I quite forgot it, so worthless seemed the gold. I left it in the cavern where a monster dragon once guarded it."

"And you brought nothing away with you?" Hagen asks incredulously.

"Only this, a curious bauble," replies Siegfried, pointing to the magic Helmet dangling from his belt, "but I know not how to use it."

Hagen knows, however, and he quickly explains that the Helmet can transform its wearer into any shape, sweep him in a trice to the ends of the earth, or even render him invisible. "You brought away nothing else?" he persists.

"Only a Ring," Siegfried answers.

"You have it with you?" Hagen can scarcely control the eagerness in his voice.

"No, the loveliest of women is wearing it," Siegfried tells him.

"That must be Brünnhilde!" Hagen mutters under his breath. Going to a door leading into another room he motions to someone within. Gutrune is radiantly beautiful when she enters bearing a drinking cup which she proffers to the guest.

"Welcome, famed hero, to our halls!" she greets him.

Siegfried bows low and accepts the cup. He pauses before drinking the contents, and with a far-away look in his eyes speaks so that no one can hear: "I quaff this cup, Brünnhilde, dearest bride, to you" Then he slowly drinks the potion while Hagen and Gunther watch him intently and Gutrune casts down her eyes in shame.

Their visitor passes his hand across his brow as though bewildered, then looks at Gutrune with a new expression. "Why do you cast down your eyes, fair lady?" he asks. Gutrune looks up in confusion, but does not answer. "Gunther!" cries Siegfried, plainly excited, "What is your sister's name?"

"Gutrune." Gunther replies quietly but his voice sounds strained.

Siegfried seizes Gutrune's hand. "I have offered myself as a friend to your brother," he tells her. "May I now offer myself to you?" Gutrune bows her head and, trembling, turns and leaves the hall. Siegfried gazes after her intently. He then turns to Gunther and asks him if he is married.

Gunther shakes his head. "I have set my heart on one I can scarcely hope to win."

"Could I be of aid?" asks Siegfried generously.

"A distant rock is her home," Gunther explains. "She lies in magic sleep, encircled by a ring of leaping flames."

"A rock . . . . encircled by flames . . . ." Siegfried repeats the words in a low voice as though striving to remember something.

"Only he who can brave that fire . . . ." Gunther begins, but Siegfried hastily breaks in. "Yes! He who can brave that fire . . . .?"

"Is Brünnhilde's true mate," Gunther finishes.

Siegfried signifies by a gesture that the mention of Brünnhilde's name means nothing to him. "I will win this maiden for you," he cries exultingly. "I have no fear of the flames. If I bring you this bride, will you, then, give me your sister, Gutrune, in marriage?" The potion is working beyond all expectation!

Gunther and his guest quickly come to an agreement. There is doubt, however, as to how Siegfried will be able to pass himself off as Gunther when he finds Brünnhilde. The magic Helmet, however, quickly solves this problem. The two men now swear "blood-brotherhood", and Siegfried insists upon setting out at once. Gunther goes with him to wait at the foot of the mountain where Siegfried is to bring Brünnhilde to him.

When the curtain rises on the next scene, we see again the mountain home of Brünnhilde and Siegfried. Brünnhilde sits gazing into the distance. Then, overcome by remembrance of Siegfried's love, she covers his ring with kisses. The sound of distant thunder is heard. Brünnhilde listens for a moment but turns again to loving contemplation of her ring. Once more the thunder rolls. This time it is louder and there is also a flash of lightning. This seems strange for the day is clear and sunny. Brünnhilde now remembers these signs and springs up. Yes! A Valkyrie is flying through the air toward Brünnhilde's Rock!

A voice calls, "Brünnhilde, Sister! Are you awake?"

"Welcome, Sister! Are you seeking me?" Brünnhilde calls joyously, running in the direction of the voice. She soon returns, bringing her

Valkyrie sister, Waltraute, with her. In her joy Brünnhilde does not at first notice that Waltraute seems anxious and distressed. "You have dared to break our father's stern decree for my sake?" she beings eagerly. "Or, tell me, has Wotan's heart softened toward me?" But Waltraute sadly shakes her head.

With quick words Brünnhilde tries to justify herself. She recalls how she disobeyed Wotan by protecting Siegmund, father of Siegfried, in his fatal combat, and for this disobedience was cast by Wotan into a long sleep from which Siegfried has now wakened her. Not heeding Waltraute's forbidding silence, she hurries on to tell her Valkyrie sister of her happiness as a mortal woman. Perhaps Waltraute has come to share a similar fate? she suggests.

"What! Share in the madness that has seized upon your soul?" cries Waltraute. "No! Other matters have led me to flout Wotan's command and seek you out." She then tells of the happenings in Valhalla since Brünnhilde's banishment. Many of these the Fates have already described while spinning their golden thread in the prelude to the opera.

Waltraute continues, "Mute sits the all-wise Father, awaiting the end of the gods. Once he was heard to mutter: 'If only Brünnhilde would return the cursed Ring to the Rhine-maidens, all would be well with the gods and with men,' so I have hastened hither, my Sister, to beg you to give up the Ring."

Brünnhilde is so absorbed by her love for Siegfried that the predicament of the gods means nothing to her and she cries, "Rather would I see Valhalla crash to ruin than part with this symbol of Siegfried's love!" Waltraute now resorts to frantic pleading, but it is useless. Brünnhilde will not listen. Defeated in her purpose, the Valkyrie cries, "You bring woe to Valhalla, faithless Sister . . . . Woe!" and she sadly takes her leave.

Brünnhilde is well satisfied with her decision and, alone once more, she quietly watches the storm cloud which envelops Waltraute on her flying steed as it rapidly vanishes in the distance. Now she notices that the ring of fire which once surrounded her as helpless maiden and has continued to protect her and Siegfried, is burning more brightly. This is a sign of danger or of Siegfried's return. The call of a horn is heard and Brünnhilde runs to the height in a transport of joy, crying, "Siegfried! Siegfried! Here!"

But it is an unknown knight who springs through the surrounding flames. (Siegfried, with the help of the magic Helmet, has taken on the form and appearance of Gunther). Without thought for her terror he

tells Brünnhilde that he has come to woo her—by force, if need be!
She stretches forth the hand that wears Siegfried's Ring.

"This Ring will protect me!" she cries. But the curse which Alberich
once placed upon the Ring continues its fatal work and it fails Brünnhilde
in her hour of need. The stranger knight snatches it from her, and drives
her before him into the cave.

When the curtain rises again it shows the entrance to the hall of the
Gibichungs at dead of night. Hagen is seated there, half sleeping, half
awake. Alberich, his father, crouches near, whispering ominously. The
vengeful Nibelung is urging his evil-hearted son never to relinquish his
efforts to regain the Ring. "Then you and I, together, will rule the
world," he promises. "You swear to win it, Hagen, my hope?"

"Cease your whimpering," Hagen answers moodily. "I swear it to
myself!" . . . . And Alberich disappears.

At dawn Hagen is awakened by a cheerful shout and Siegfried enters.
He is in the act of removing the magic Helmet which, in a flash, has
brought him back from the foot of the mountain where he left
Brünnhilde with Gunther.

"Ho, Siegfried, speedy hero! Were you successful?" inquires Hagen.

Siegfried is in great good humor and rather boisterously relates his
adventures. He adds that Gunther is now returning to these lordly halls
with the bride Siegfried has won for him. Gutrune comes forth to greet
him and together the loving pair enter the hall.

Hagen retires to the back and, standing on a grassy mound, sounds
his horn to summon the vassals. They come running from all directions.
When they are gathered together, Hagen tells them of Gunther's
approaching wedding and bids them welcome him and the bride he
has won!

As Gunther's boat is sighted, the vassals greet him and Brünnhilde
with rousing cheers. He assists her from the boat, offers her his hand,
and proudly leads her forward as his subjects bow low. But Brünnhilde
is pale as death and walks with downcast eyes. She seems not to hear the
cheering and the glad greetings of those around her.

"Why is Gunther's bride so pale and sad?" they ask each other in
wonder.

Siegfried and Gutrune, followed by a train of attendant maidens, now
come from the great hall. Siegfried steps forward as if to a stranger,
asking, "What clouds Brünnhilde's brow?"

Brünnhilde looks up, startled to hear the voice of her beloved.

"Siegfried!" she cries, "You . . . . here!" and she sways as though with faintness. But there is no answering look of recognition in his eyes.

"This is Gutrune, Gunther's mild-eyed sister," he says, "who is to be my mate as Gunther is to be yours."

"Gunther . . . . I? . . . . You lie!" Brünnhilde looks about her wildly. Seeing the Ring on Siegfried's finger, she cries fiercely, "That Ring! How came you by it? He," pointing toward Gunther, "but lately tore it from me!" Brünnhilde still believes that it was Gunther who came through the ring of fire and wooed her by force, and she feels that Siegfried has betrayed her. Siegfried examines the Ring curiously. Owing to the potion of forgetfulness, he does not remember wresting it from Brünnhilde.

Gunther's suspicions are aroused at these words and he begins to wonder if Siegfried, his new-found friend, may have played him false. He charges him with this but Siegfried swears on a spear's point that he carried out his mission for Gunther exactly as he promised. Turning away impatiently, he leads Gutrune from the scene.

The vassals cannot understand why this home-coming of their King has turned out so strangely. They had expected it to be a joyful and festive occasion and, disappointed, they slowly take their departure. Hagen, cause of all this confusion, stands silently in the background, watching and waiting.

Brünnhilde, Gunther, and Hagen remain in the hall alone. Brünnhilde, completely distracted, resorts to a lie for she is overcome by a sudden desire to be avenged on Siegfried. She declares that the hero broke his promise to Gunther by making love to her while on his mission to win her for his friend. This is not true as Siegfried has sworn. But Brünnhilde is almost mad with grief and bewilderment and now insists that Siegfried must die!

Hagen, pleased with the course of events, whispers to her, "Show me some way to make Siegfried weak in my hands, for well I know his strength." Brünnhilde then tells him that she has made Siegfried invulnerable, except in the back. "There a spear could strike him!" she says.

But Gunther objects, "Betrayed though I be, we swore blood-brotherhood, Siegfried and I. For the sake of my honor, this must not be!"

Hagen refuses to listen to him. "Nothing now will suffice but Siegfried's death!" he says grimly.

"Siegfried's death!" Gunther repeats the two words with horror in his voice. "But what of my sister?" he asks.

"To lighten her grief and to hide the true deed from her, we will go tomorrow on a hunting party," Hagen tells him. "Siegfried will stray from the rest and will be brought home, having been 'killed by a wild boar'." Thus Hagen plots, and Gunther weakly yields.

The next scene is a lovely spot by the River Rhine. The Rhine-maidens are swimming about as they play in the waters and sing a light-hearted song.

Play Song of the Rhine-maidens

They hear the call of a horn.

Horn Theme

The sound of the horn grows louder and Siegfried appears on the bank. He is a handsome young hunter and the Rhine-maidens call to him to attract his attention. He answers them, amused by their prattle. When one of them presently asks him for his Ring, he carelessly slips it from his finger. It means nothing to him for he has quite forgotten that he ever gave it to Brünnhilde with his love. He thinks these pretty maidens in the water may as well have it to play with.

But now the Rhine-maidens, with the precious Ring almost within their grasp, make a grave mistake. They tell Siegfried of the curse attached to the Ring, and the danger that lies in wearing it. This pricks his vanity.

"Hah! Afraid of a ring? Not I," he scoffs and puts it back on his finger. The Rhine-maidens warn him once again and then swim away while Siegfried looks after them curiously.

Hagen, Gunther, and the rest of the hunting-party now come in sight and Siegfried hails them. "Heh, it is cool and restful by the river's bank," he shouts. "Bide here with me."

They gather around, stretching out under the trees, while flagons are filled and passed around. Hagen is watchful, ready to strike the fatal blow at Siegfried, but Gunther is bathed in gloom for the death of his friend is not to his liking. Siegfried, unsuspecting, is in a mirthful mood, and laughingly tells of his meeting with the pretty river nymphs.

Seeing that Gunther is troubled, Siegfried asks him if he would not like to hear some of his early adventures, for Hagen's potion has not made him forget all his early life. Gunther assents, and Siegfried proves to be a good story-teller. He amuses the men with his accounts of Mime, his adventure with the dragon, the song of the wood-bird, the treasure in the cave, and the magic Helmet and Ring he brought away with him.

As he comes to that part of his life which Hagen's magic potion has clouded, Hagen, unnoticed by anyone, refills the hero's cup with another draught, one which will bring back remembrance. Siegfried drinks it. He then tells of his pursuit of the beautiful maiden who lay in magic sleep on a mountain top and goes on, with growing rapture, to describe Brünnhilde and his happiness with her.

Gunther now realizes to his shame that he and his sister, Gutrune, have been dupes of Hagen's wicked designs, and that Siegfried has innocently aided their plans at the cost of his own honor and happiness.

While Siegfried is still speaking of Brünnhilde, two black ravens start up from the bushes nearby and circle above his head.

"Can you read that omen aright?" demands Hagen harshly. A shudder passes over all those present. Siegfried turns his back to Hagen and leaning forward, gazes intently at these omens of death. At this moment Hagen, with a powerful lunge, strikes his spear into Siegfried's back . . . . !

"Hagen, what have you done!" cries Gunther in distress. The men spring up in wild excitement.

"It is retribution," says Hagen coolly, and walks away.

Gunther, in anguish, bends over his friend. The others gather around in mute sympathy. After a time Siegfried opens his eyes, now glazed with death, and brokenly speaks of his love for Brünnhilde, imagining that she is calling to him.

Evening falls. The moon breaks through the clouds and lights the scene. The men solemnly wrap the body of their dead comrade in a cloak, raise him upon their shoulders, and start on their weary march toward home. Gunther, overcome with grief, goes with them. Mists rise from the Rhine and envelop the scene. An impressive funeral march is intoned as they go on until lost to sight.

The music gradually changes as the mists disperse and we see once more the hall of the Gibichungs. Moonlight is glittering on the waters of the Rhine. Gutrune appears, waiting anxiously for the return of the hunters. She is filled with a foreboding she cannot explain. "Was that the sound of a horn?" she says half aloud. "No . . . . they return not yet !"

Hagen's voice breaks the stillness. "Hoiho! Bring on the torches. Fair booty have we here!"

Servitors hurry forward with torches and firebrands and Hagen appears. When Gutrune sees him she is suddenly overcome with fright. "What does this mean?" she asks. "I do not hear Siegfried's horn!" As Hagen fails to reply, she peers into the gloom where the hunting party approaches with solemn tread. "What bring they there?" she asks with growing dread.

Hagen's reply is heartless. "A wild boar's victim they bring there—your lover's corpse."

Gutrune cries out in anguish and, as the procession enters the hall, throws herself upon the body of Siegfried. Hagen creeps forward to take the Ring but Gunther pushes him back fiercely. "Away, you wretch!" he cries. "Do not touch what is ours. This Ring is now a part of Gutrune's dowry."

Hagen draws his sword. "As heir to the Ring which first belonged to my father, Alberich, I claim it!" At these words Gunther springs upon him, but is killed by a blow from Hagen's sword. Hagen now leaps forward to tear the Ring from Siegfried's finger, but the hand of the dead man is suddenly thrust upward. Hagen recoils and all cry out in terror.

Brünnhilde now enters with a firm and solemn tread. All gaze upon her in awed silence as she slowly makes her way to Siegfried's side and gazes with tragic sorrow upon his countenance. Gradually her expression changes to one of peace—even of exaltation as with unfaltering voice she begins an invocation to Wotan, chief of all the gods.

"Oh Wotan; Mightiest god! Even you were helpless to stay the curse of the Ring. Even your best loved hero had to die, that one woman might learn the truth. I see it all now . . . . all things are clear." She turns with great solemnity to the assembled vassals and bids them erect a funeral pyre. Having done this, she orders Siegfried's body to be placed upon it and the faggots to be lighted.

Brünnhilde now calls for her horse, Grane, which is brought. She then approaches the body of Siegfried and slowly draws the Ring from his finger. Holding it up, she proclaims: "Here I hold my dowry once again! I hold it but to give it up. Heed, ye Rhine-maidens, this is yours. Purged clean by the red flames of this funeral pyre, the Ring at last shall be freed from its fatal curse!" She places the Ring on her finger, takes the bridle of her steed in her hand, and with him, plunges into the seething flames. Instinctively the vassals fall on their knees.

Hagen alone is unmoved. Still beset by a mad desire for the Ring, he leaps forward to snatch it from the consuming flames. As he does so the waters of the Rhine rise in flood and quench the fire. On the waves ride the three Rhine-maidens who have heard Brünnhilde's call. One of them grasps the false Hagen by the throat and draws him down under the black waters. Another finds the Ring and, holding it up in triumph, the three Rhine-maidens swim away, rejoicing.

A new wonder now appears. In the flaming sky is seen a vision of Valhalla where the gods sit in solemn circle, awaiting their doom. The flames grow fiercer. They reach ever upward, enveloping the stronghold, until the swaying towers crash in ruin. The twilight of the gods has come!

The Fall of Valhalla

Now the music changes to sound a note of peace and hope. It seems to say: "A new days comes."

255

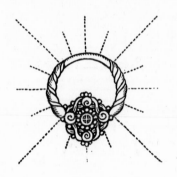

HALF~MINUTE HISTORIES

The Prize Song or The Mastersingers

COMPOSED by Richard Wagner. German composer. b. Leipsic, May 22, 1813; d. Venice, Feb. 13, 1883. FIRST PERFORMANCE: Munich, June 21, 1868, Hans von Bülow conducting. London, Drury Lane, May 30, 1882, Hans Richter conducting. First performance in America, Metropolitan Opera House, New York, Jan. 4, 1886, with Emil Fischer as *Hans Sachs;* Albert Stritt as *Walther;* Auguste Seidl-Krauss as *Eva;* Otto Kemlitz as *Beckmesser.* Anton Seidl conducting.

CAST FOR ORIGINAL PERFORMANCE IN MUNICH

Hans Sachs, the cobbler poet	. . . bass	. . . . . . Franz Betz
Walther, a young knight	. . . . . tenor	. . . . . Franz Nachbaur
Beckmesser, a mastersinger	. . . . baritone	. . . . . . Herr Hölzl
David, Sachs's apprentice	. . . tenor	. . . . . Carl Schlosser
Eva	. . . . soprano	. . . . Mlle. Mallinger
Magdalena, her companion	. . . . mezzo	. . . . . . Mme. Diez

The scene is laid in Nuremberg in the sixteenth century.

The Mastersingers (Die Meistersinger) is Wagner's only comic opera. It presents a delightful and amusing picture of Nuremberg at the time when the famous Mastersingers Guild was at the height of its influence and importance. In the rule-ridden compositions of the Guild the composer found an answer to his critics who could find nothing to praise in his revolutionary ideas regarding opera.

In his advice to Hölzl who created the role of Beckmesser, a spiteful person who causes Walther to fail in his first hearing before the Guild, Wagner said: "Act like any captious critic."

Wagner preferred to call his operas "music dramas" because of the close union of words, music, and dramatic action. He is the only composer who has written his own librettos. The words of each of his operas are the result of extensive study of folk lore, legend, and history.

GUIDE TO PRONUNCIATION

Die Meistersinger	. . . . Dee My'-stir-singer
Hans Sachs	. . . . Hans Socks
Fritz Kothner	. . . . Fritz Coat'-ner
Veit Pogner	. . . . Vite Pog-ner

Madame Butterfly

COMPOSED by Giacomo Puccini. Italian composer. b. Lucca, June 22, 1858; d. Brussels, Nov. 29, 1924. FIRST PERFORMANCE: La Scala, Milan, Feb. 17, 1904, with Mme. Storchio, Zenatello and De Luca. Cleofante Campanini conducted who later was opera conductor in New York and Chicago. First London performance July 10, 1905, with Emmy Destinn, Caruso and Scotti, Campanini conducting. First time in America in a series of performances in English by Savage Grand Opera Company, Garden Theater, New York, autumn of 1906. Metropolitan Opera House première, Feb. 11, 1907, sung in Italian in the presence of the composer, Arturo Vigna conducting.

CAST FOR METROPOLITAN PREMIÈRE

Cio-Cio-San (Madame Butterfly) .	soprano	Geraldine Farrar
Suzuki	mezzo-soprano .	Louise Homer
Pinkerton	tenor	Caruso
Sharpless	baritone	Scotti
Goro	tenor	Reiss

The scene is laid in Japan.

Puccini visited this country especially for the Metropolitan production of his opera and to direct rehearsals. Although at that time Miss Farrar was one of the most popular opera stars, the composer expressed himself as greatly displeased with her singing when he first heard her in rehearsal. The public, however, acclaimed her *Butterfly* as one of her greatest triumphs.

Puccini was at the height of his fame when he composed *Madame Butterfly*, but the first performance in Milan was so disliked by the public that he withdrew all rights of performance. With slight changes it was put on at Brescia a few months later, and since then has become a favorite opera wherever opera is sung.

Other operas by Puccini most frequently performed are *La Bohème* and *La Tosca*.

GUIDE TO PRONUNCIATION

Giacomo Puccini . . .	(G like soft J) Jee-ah'-ko-mo Poo-chee'-nee
Cio-Cio-San	Cho-Cho-San
Suzuki	Soo-zoo'-kee
Goro	G as in *go*

Carmen

COMPOSED by Georges Bizet, French composer. b. Paris, Oct. 25, 1838; d. Bougival near Paris, June 3, 1875. FIRST PERFORMANCE: Opera Comique, Paris, March 3, 1875. Mme. Galli-Marie created the title role. First London performance (sung in Italian) with Minnie Hauck as *Carmen*; Italo Campanini as *Don José*; Del Puente as *Escamillo*; Alvina Valleria as *Micaela*. First performance in the United States, Academy of Music, New York, Oct. 23, 1879, with Minnie Hauck, Campanini, and Del Puente.

CAST FOR ORIGINAL PERFORMANCE IN PARIS

Don José, a corporal	tenor	Lherie
Escamillo, toreador	baritone	Bouhy
Dancairo, smuggler	tenor	Poitl
Remendado, smuggler	tenor	Banolt
Zuniga, captain	bass	Dufriche
Morales, corporal	baritone	Duvernoy
Carmen, a gypsy	mezzo-soprano	Galli-Marie
Micaela, village maiden	soprano	Chapuy
Frasquita ⎱ gypsies	soprano	Ducasse
Mercedes ⎰	soprano	Chevalier

The scene is laid in Spain about 1820.

The role of *Carmen* has had many famous interpreters. Calvé made her New York debut in this role at the Metropolitan, Dec. 20, 1893, with Jean de Reszke as *Don José* and Emma Eames as *Micaela*.

The composer's fame rests chiefly on this opera. It was not a success at first, but since then has become popular all over the world. Bizet died at thirty-six, only three months after the first performance. The opera is based on a novel by Prosper Merimée, a French author, but contains much characteristic Spanish music.

Bizet is also well known for his "L'Arlesiénne" Suite, more popular in concert form for orchestra alone than as an opera. Based on "The Woman of Arles" by Daudet.

GUIDE TO PRONUNCIATION

Georges Bizet	Geor-je Bee'-zay
Don José	Don Ho-zay'
Escamillo	Es-ka-mil'-lo
Zuniga	Zu-nee'-ga
Lillas Pastia	Lil-las Pas'-tia
Morales	Mor-ah-lees'
Micaela	Mick-ah-ai'-la
Dancairo	Dan-kah-eer'-o
Remendado	Rem-en-dah'-do

Faust

COMPOSED by Charles François Gounod. French composer. b. Paris, June 17, 1818. d. there, Oct. 17, 1893. FIRST PERFORMANCE: Théâtre Lyrique, Paris, March 19, 1859. First London performance, June 11, 1863. First performance in America, Academy of Music, New York, Nov. 25, 1863. When the Metropolitan Opera House was built, *Faust* was selected for the opening night, Oct. 22, 1883, sung in Italian with Christine Nilsson as *Marguerite;* Sofia Scalchi as *Siebel;* Italo Campanini as *Faust;* Signor Novara as *Mephistopheles.*

CAST FOR THE ORIGINAL PERFORMANCE IN PARIS

Faust	tenor	Barbot
Mephistopheles	bass	Balanqué
Marguerite	soprano	Mme. Miolan-Carvalho
Valentine, her brother	baritone	Regnal
Siebel, a village youth	mezzo-soprano	Mlle. Fiavre
Martha	mezzo-soprano	Mme. Duclos

The scene is a town in Germany in the sixteenth century.

The story of the opera is founded on the first part of Goethe's great dramatic poem, *Faust.* In Paris no other opera has equalled its continued popularity. It is the work by which the composer is best known. His next most popular opera is *Romeo and Juliet.*

It was natural that the story with its element of religious mysticism should have appealed to Gounod. When he was twenty-five he began to study theology so seriously that many of his friends expected him to take holy orders, but other ambitions prevailed. Although he wrote church works early in his career, he soon turned to the theatre for his inspiration, and found in opera the best medium for his musical genius.

The rôles of *Marguerite, Faust,* and *Mephistopheles* have enlisted the greatest singers since the day the opera was first heard.

GUIDE TO PRONUNCIATION

Gounod	Goo'-no
Siebel	See'-bel

Il Trovatore

COMPOSED by Giuseppe Verdi. Italian composer. b. at Le Roncole near Busseto, Oct. 10, 1813; d. Milan, Jan. 27, 1901. FIRST PERFORMANCE: Apollo Theatre, Rome, Jan. 19, 1853. First London performance, Covent Garden, May 17, 1855, in English as *The Gypsy's Vengeance.* First sung in Paris in 1857 as *Le Trouvère.* First time in America, Academy of Music, New York, May 2, 1855, with the following cast:

Manrico, a young chieftain of Biscay .	tenor	Pasquale Brignoli
Leonora, beloved of Manrico	soprano . .	Signora Steffanone
Azucena, the old gypsy	contralto . .	Signorina Vestvali
Count di Luna of Arragon	baritone	Amodio

The scene is laid in the Spanish provinces of Arragon and Biscay in the beginning of the fifteenth century.

Il Trovatore or *The Troubadour* was first produced in Rome in the same year as Verdi's *La Traviata,* but unlike the latter, was at once a success. It is full of melodies which the entire world has learned to hum and love. *The Anvil Chorus,* the duet *Home to Our Mountains,* and the *Troubadour's Addio* from his prison tower, are among the most familiar numbers.

This opera was composed two years after Verdi's *Rigoletto* and fourteen years before *Aïda.* It contains one of the greatest contralto rôles in all opera, that of *Azucena,* the old gypsy who pretends to be Manrico's mother.

GUIDE TO PRONUNCIATION

Giuseppe Verdi	(G like a soft J) Jee-sep'-pa Vair'-dee
Manrico	Man-ree'-ko
Azucena	Ah-zoo-chain'-a

Lohengrin

COMPOSED by Richard Wagner. German composer. b. Leipsic, May 22, 1813; d. Venice, Feb. 13, 1883. FIRST PERFORMANCE: Weimar, Germany, Aug. 26, 1850, under Franz Liszt. First London performance, Covent Garden, May 8, 1875; New York, Stadt Theater on the Bowery, April 3, 1871; first Metropolitan Opera performance, Nov. 7, 1883, in Italian, with Nilsson as *Elsa;* Fursch-Madi as *Ortrud;* Campanini as *Lohengrin;* first time in German according to composer's traditions at Metropolitan, Dec. 3, 1884, Dr. Leopold Damrosch conducting, with Seidl-Krauss as *Elsa;* Marianne Brandt as *Ortrud;* Anton Schott as *Lohengrin.*

CAST OF ORIGINAL PRODUCTION IN WEIMAR

Henry, the Fowler, King	bass	Hofer
Lohengrin	tenor	Beck
Elsa, Princess of Brabant	soprano	Frau Agathe
Ortrud, wife of Telramund	mezzo-soprano	Frl. Fastlinger
Count Telramund	baritone	Milde

The scene is laid in Antwerp in the first half of tenth century.

Wagner was exiled from Germany for eleven years due to his political activities at Dresden in 1849, where he was director of the opera. He spent his exile first in Paris where *Lohengrin* was begun; completed the score in Switzerland. This opera came after *Rienzi, The Flying Dutchman,* and *Tannhäuser.* Based on his studies of Teutonic myths, the Arthurian legends, and the Holy Grail (which he elaborated as the theme of his last opera, *Parsifal.*)

Lohengrin had its first public hearing through the efforts of his staunch supporter, Franz Liszt, the composer-pianist, whose daughter Cosima, became Wagner's second wife. Although *Lohengrin* is credited as the first opera to bring the composer wider recognition, this came slowly. It took 19 years to reach Italy; 25 years to reach London, and Paris waited 41 years to hear what has become one of Wagner's most popular operas.

GUIDE TO PRONUNCIATION

Brabant	Brah-bant′
Telramund	Tel′-ra-mund
Ortrud	Or′-trood

Aïda

COMPOSED by Giuseppe Verdi. Italian composer. b. at Le Roncole near Busseto, Oct. 10, 1813; d. Milan, Jan. 27, 1901. *Aïda* composed at command of the Khedive of Egypt. FIRST PERFORMANCE: Cairo, Egypt, Dec. 24, 1871. First performance in Europe at La Scala, Milan, Feb. 8, 1872, under the direction of the composer. Reached New York before being heard in any of the great European opera houses except La Scala. Produced by Max Strakosch at the Academy of Music, Nov. 26, 1873, with the following brilliant cast:

Aïda, Ethiopian slave	soprano	Octavia Torriani
Amneris, Pharaoh's daughter	mezzo-soprano	Anna Louise Cary
Radames, a young warrior	tenor	Italo Campanini
Amonasro, King of Ethiopia	baritone	Victor Maurel
Ramphis, the High Priest	bass	Nannetti
Pharaoh, the king	bass	Scolari

The scene is laid in Memphis and Thebes when the Pharaohs were in power.

Paris did not hear *Aïda* until 1876, and two months later it was first produced at Covent Garden, London, June 22, 1876.

The Khedive of Egypt had had a magnificent opera house built at Cairo for which he wanted an opera on an Egyptian subject. He turned to Italy's "grand old man" of opera, Verdi, who was already well along in years, to compose a work based on an episode in Egyptian history, and *Aïda* was the result.

This opera proved to be a turning-point in Verdi's long career for it marks a distinct step forward in the dramatic character of his music. He even uses the "leading motive" idea instituted by Wagner. The theme for *Aïda* is sounded in the orchestra whenever she is about to appear. An oriental flavor is introduced in the rhythms and harmonies of the dances in the pageant scene and the temple dances of the priestesses.

Among the operas preceding *Aïda* were *Ernani* (1844); *Rigoletto* (1851), *Il Trovatore* and *La Traviata* (1853), *Masked Ball* (1859) and *Don Carlos* (1867).

GUIDE TO PRONUNCIATION

Aïda	Ah-ee'-dah
Amneris	Ahm-nair'-iss
Radames	Rah-da-maize'
Amonasro	A-mon-aas'-ro
Ramphis	Ramm'-fiss
Gorge of Napata	Nah-pah-tah'

La Bohème

COMPOSED by Giacomo Puccini. Italian composer. b. Lucca, June 22, 1858; d. Brussels, Nov. 29, 1924. FIRST PERFORMANCE: Teatro Regio, Turin, Feb. 1, 1896, conducted by Toscanini. Sung in English as *The Bohemians,* Manchester, England, April 22, 1897; first time Covent Garden, London (in English), Oct. 2, 1897; first time in Italian, Covent Garden, July 1, 1899, with Melba as *Mimi.*

La Bohème came to America via San Francisco, March, 1898 with an Italian touring company which also produced the opera in New York at Wallach's Theatre, May 16, 1898. Sung in English by Henry W. Savage's Castle Square Opera Company Nov. 20, 1898. Presented first time at Metropolitan (sung in Italian) Dec. 26, 1900, with the following brilliant cast:

METROPOLITAN OPERA CAST

Rudolph, a poet	tenor	Albert Saléza
Marcel, a painter	baritone	Giuseppe Campanari
Colline, a philosopher	bass	Marcel Journet
Schaunard, a musician	baritone	Charles Gilibert
Mimi, friend to Rudolph	soprano	Nellie Melba
Musetta, a grisette	soprano	Fritzi Scheff

The scene is laid in Paris about 1840.

Unfortunately Miss Scheff was ill, and her place was taken by Miss Occhiolini, not a member of the Metropolitan. But *Musetta* became one of Miss Scheff's most popular rôles later. The opera based on scenes from Murger's novel, *La Vie de Bohème.* Several years spent by composer and librettists to reduce usable scenes to limited length, but result is one of the most entertaining opera stories in existence, picturing the life of four youthful artists in the Latin Quarter in Paris.

Puccini's chief teacher was Ponchielli, composer of *La Gioconda.* The success of *La Bohème* definitely placed Puccini at the head of the modern Italian composers. It followed three less successful operas: *Le Villi* (1884); *Edgar* (1889) and *Manon Lescaut* (1893).

GUIDE TO PRONUNCIATION

Marcel	Mar-sell'
Colline	Col-leen'
Schaunard	Sho-naar
Mimi	Mee'-mee

Tristan and Isolde

COMPOSED by Richard Wagner. German composer. b. Leipsic, May 22, 1813; d. Venice, Feb. 13, 1883. FIRST PERFORMANCE: Munich, June 10, 1865, Hans von Bülow conducting. Drury Lane, London, June 20, 1882. First time in America, Metropolitan Opera House, New York, Dec. 1, 1886, with Anton Seidl conducting the following brilliant cast:

METROPOLITAN OPERA CAST

Tristan, a knight of Cornwall . . .	tenor	Albert Niemann
Isolde, an Irish princess	soprano	Lilli Lehmann
King Mark	bass	Emil Fischer
Kurvenal, retainer of Tristan . . .	baritone . . .	Adolf Robinson
Melot	bass . . .	Rodolph von Milde
Brangaene, Isolde's attendant . . .	contralto . . .	Marianne Brandt

The scene is laid in Cornwall and Brittany in the tenth century.

This ancient Irish legend appealed to the poetic nature of Wagner as a fitting subject for a romantic opera. He began the score in 1857. To do this he interrupted his work on *The Nibelung's Ring* after having completed the first two operas and having begun *Siegfried*. Greatly discouraged at the constant difficulties placed in his way, he had come to the conclusion that the *Ring Cycle* had little prospect of ever being produced. "I must this time accomplish a miracle in order to make the world believe in me," he wrote to his friend Liszt.

Wagner was in dire poverty at the time and hoped that *Tristan* would soon bring him financial returns. Little did he dream that seven years would elapse before its first performance. The beautiful second act was written in Venice amidst agreeable surroundings, but the difficulties which beset the exiled composer terminated his sojourn there, and it was in Switzerland on the Lake of Lucerne that the score was finally completed in August, 1859.

GUIDE TO PRONUNCIATION

Isolde	E-sol'-duh
Kurvenal	Koor'-va-nahl
Melot	Mel'-ott
Brangaene	Brung-gain'-uh

Rigoletto

COMPOSED by Giuseppe Verdi. Italian composer. b. Le Roncole near Busseto, Oct. 10, 1813. d. Milan, Jan. 27, 1901. FIRST PERFORMANCE: Teatro La Fenice, Venice, March 11, 1851. First at Covent Garden, London, May 15, 1853, with Giuseppe Mario as the *Duke* and Giorgio Ronconi as *Rigoletto,* considered the greatest tenor and baritone of their day. They gave a performance which has gone down in history as a superlative achievement.

First performance in America, Academy of Music, Feb. 19, 1855, under the management of Ole Bull, the famous violinist, who tried to be an opera impresario for a short and disastrous period. The cast of this performance is of extraordinary interest since it involved the unofficial operatic debut of Adelina Patti who, under the name of "Patti Strakosch" sang the small contralto rôle of *Maddelene,* although only twelve years old at that time. The reason for the name used for program purposes was that Maurice Strakosch was the husband of Adelina's older sister, Amalia, and was Patti's teacher and manager. She appeared in addition to this lone operatic appearance in many concerts during the fifties, before she made her formal debut at the Academy of Music in 1859.

THE CAST

Rigoletto, court jester	baritone	Ettore Barili
		(half-brother to Patti)
Duke of Mantua	tenor	Bolcioni
Gilda, Rigoletto's daughter	soprano	Bertucca Maretzek
Maddelene	contralto	Patti Strakosch

The scene is Mantua, early sixteenth century.

The opera is based on Victor Hugo's drama, *Le Roi s'amuse.* When the libretto was ready, the Italian police refused to permit a king (Francis I) to be represented on the stage. After many difficulties, a compromise was effected, the "king" became a "duke", and the scene was transferred from Paris to Mantua. Verdi, long impatient at the delay, wrote furiously, completing the entire score in forty days.

At rehearsal time, the tenor found a blank instead of his final solo, *La donna è mobile* (see p. 171). "Just wait, be patient," Verdi told him. Not until the day before the final rehearsal was the music given to him and then under an oath of secrecy. Verdi knew that everyone in Venice would be singing it, and so they did, the day after the performance!

GUIDE TO PRONUNCIATION

Gilda	(Soft J sound) Jil'-da
Giovanna	(Soft J sound) Jo-vann'-a
Maddelene	Mad-da-lain'-a
Sparafucile	Spaar-ah-foo-tcee'-lee

The Barber of Seville

COMPOSED by Gioachino Rossini. Italian composer. b. Pesaro, Feb. 29, 1792; d. Ruelle, near Paris, Nov. 13, 1868. FIRST PERFORMANCE: Teatro Argentina, Rome, Feb. 5, 1816. Manual Garcia, most famous tenor of his day, created the rôle of the *Count* so successfully that the opera went with him to London, King's Theatre, March 10, 1818; and to Paris, 1819.

In America first sung at the Park Theatre, New York, in English, May 3, 1819; at the same theatre six years later, in Italian, with Garcia, the tenor. The remarkable cast included three other members of his family, his daughter (then only seventeen, known in musical history as Mme. Malibran), his son, and Manual's wife.

THE GARCIA CAST

Count Almaviva	tenor	Manual Garcia
Dr. Bartolo	bass	Rosich
Rosina, his ward	soprano	Maria Garcia (Malibran)
Figaro, the barber	baritone	Manual Garcia (Manual's son)
Don Basilio, music master	bass	Agrisani
Berta	mezzo	Signora Garcia

The scene is in Seville in the eighteenth century.

The first time *The Barber* was sung at the Metropolitan (November, 1883), Mme. Sembrich was *Rosina*.

The composer was only twenty-five when he wrote this opera based on the French comedy of Beaumarchais, but Rossini soon found himself in trouble owing to the fact that Paisiello, an older composer, had used the same play for an opera. Rossini finally obtained permission to use it, and the opera was composed and put into production inside of a month.

The first performance brought hisses, instigated by Paisiello's friends who were jealous of Rossini's success, and partly due to what the public considered unwarranted musical innovations, so modern did this work appear to be! It has been popular for 130 years, and is the best known and best liked of his fifty-three operas.

GUIDE TO PRONUNCIATION

Gioachino Rossini	(soft J) Jo-a-keen'-o Ro-see'-nee
Figaro	Fig'-ah-ro
Doctor Bartolo	Bar'-to-lo
Rosina	Ro-zeen'-a

The Rhinegold

COMPOSED by Richard Wagner. German composer. b. Leipsic, May 22, 1813; d. Venice, Feb. 13, 1883. FIRST PERFORMANCE: Munich, Sept. 22, 1869. First time as a part of the complete *Ring Cycle* opening the Baireuth Festival, Aug. 13, 1876, Hans Richter conducting. First time in London, Her Majesty's Theatre, May 5, 1882, Anton Seidl conducting. First time in America, Metropolitan Opera House, New York, Jan. 4, 1889, Seidl conducting. Emil Fischer as *Wotan;* Max Alvary as *Loki;* Joseph Beck as *Alberich;* Fanny Moran-Olden as *Fricka.*

The Rhinegold is the first of the four operas constituting *The Nibelung's Ring.* The first performance of the complete *Ring Cycle* was the opening event of the first Baireuth Festival where the *Festspielhaus* (Festival Opera House) had been built according to Wagner's plan for the performance of his operas under ideal conditions. Notables from all over the world were present on that occasion.

CAST FOR THE FIRST BAIREUTH PERFORMANCE

Wotan	Gods	bass	Franz Betz
Loki		tenor	Heinrich Vogl
Donner		bass	Eugen Gura
Froh		tenor	Georg Unger
Alberich	Nibelungs	baritone	Carl Hill
Mime		tenor	Carl Schlosser
Fafner	Giants	bass	F. von Reichenberg
Fasolt		baritone	Albert Eilers
Fricka	Goddesses	soprano	Frederike Grün-Sadler
Freia		soprano	Marie Haupt
Erda		contralto	Luise Jaïde
Woglinde	Rhine-maidens	soprano	Lilli Lehmann
Wellgunde		soprano	Marie Lehmann
Flosshilde		mezzo-soprano	Minna Lammert

Scenes: Bottom of the River Rhine; on the heights with a view of Valhalla; the caverns of Nibelheim.

GUIDE TO PRONUNCIATION

Wotan	Vo-tahn
Loki	Low-ki

(*Loge* is the German form, the G pronounced like a soft J—Loj-uh)

Mime	Mee-muh
Fricka	Free-kah
Freia	Fry-uh

The Valkyrie

COMPOSED by Richard Wagner. German composer. b. Leipsic, May 22, 1813; d. Venice, Feb. 13, 1883. FIRST PERFORMANCE: Munich, June 26, 1870, with Heinrich Vogl and his wife as *Siegmund* and *Sieglinde*. First adequate performance in its rightful place as second opera of the *Ring Cycle*, Baireuth, Aug. 14, 1876, Hans Richter conducting. London, Her Majesty's Theatre, May 6, 1882, Anton Seidl conducting.

First important performance in America, Metropolitan Opera House, New York, Jan. 30, 1885, conducted by Dr. Leopold Damrosch. Materna as *Brünnhilde* who had sung in the original Baireuth production; Seidl-Krauss as *Sieglinde*, Anton Schott as *Siegmund*, and Marianne Brandt as *Fricka*. Eight years earlier a poor performance had been given at the Academy of Music, New York, under Adolph Neuendorff.

CAST OF FIRST BAIREUTH PERFORMANCE

Siegmund	tenor	Albert Niemann
Hunding	bass	Niering
Wotan	bass	Franz Betz
Sieglinde	soprano	Frl. Schefzky
Brünnhilde, the Valkyrie	soprano	Amalia Materna
Fricka	soprano	Grün-Sadler

Scenes: Hunding's hut. A mountain gorge. Brünnhilde's Rock.

New themes introduced are the love music of *Siegmund* and *Sieglinde* and their individual themes; the *Hunding* theme, music pertaining to the *Valkyries* (Brünnhilde and her sisters), and the music of the *fire charm* which closes the opera. A popular concert number is *The Ride of the Valkyries* beginning the third act.

To the many themes relating to objects and already introduced in *The Rhinegold* such as the *gold* theme, the *Ring* theme, etc., is added the *sword* theme, heard again importantly in the third opera of the *Ring Cycle* when the sword is mended by *Siegfried*, son of *Siegmund*.

GUIDE TO PRONUNCIATION

The Valkyrie	The Val-keer-y
(The German form is *Die Walküre*, pronounced Dee Val-kuer-uh)	
Siegmund	Seeg-mund
Sieglinde	Seeg-lin'-duh
Brünnhilde	Brin-hil'-duh
Waltraute	Val-trow'-tuh
Nothung (the sword)	No'-toong

Siegfried

COMPOSED by Richard Wagner. German composer. b. Leipsic, May 22, 1813; d. Venice, Feb. 13, 1883. FIRST PERFORMANCE: Baireuth, Aug. 16, 1876, Hans Richter conducting. London, Her Majesty's Theatre, May 7, 1882, Anton Seidl conducting. First performance in America, Metropolitan Opera House, New York, Nov. 9, 1887, Seidl conducting, with Lille Lehmann as *Brünnhilde;* Max Alvary as *Siegfried;* and Emil Fischer as *Wotan.*

CAST OF ORIGINAL BAIREUTH PERFORMANCE

Siegfried	tenor	Georg Unger
Mime	tenor	Carl Schlosser
Wotan (as the Wanderer)	bass	Franz Betz
Alberich	baritone	Carl Hill
Fafner	bass	F. von Reichenberg
Erda	contralto	Luise Jaïda
Brünnhilde	soprano	Amalia Materna

Scenes: Mime's cave. The forest. Wild mountain region. Brünnhilde's Rock.

Siegfried is the third opera of *The Nibelung's Ring.* The title rôle is one of the most taxing written for the tenor voice, and has enlisted the greatest interpreters of Wagnerian rôles. The opera is said to have been Wagner's favorite, because in it he most nearly realized his ideal of having the orchestral music tell the story. It weaves a wonderful tapestry of sound, relating by means of the musical themes events long past (as revealed in *The Rhinegold* and *The Valkyrie*) and prophesying the future.

This opera is often spoken of as "the forest drama" since it all takes place out of doors, with the exception of Mime's cave which lies in the depths of a forest. This same forest hides the lair of the dragon, Fafner, first known in *The Rhinegold* as one of the giants. Music that is beautiful and of a highly original nature is added to the themes already familiar. The part most frequently heard as a concert piece is the scene, *Forest Murmurs,* during which Siegfried learns about Brünnhilde from the singing of a bird.

GUIDE TO PRONUNCIATION

Siegfried	Seeg-freed
Mime	Mee′-muh

Die Götterdämmerung

COMPOSED by Richard Wagner. German composer. b. Leipsic, May 22, 1813; d. Venice, Feb. 13, 1883. Last of the four operas in *The Nibelung's Ring*. FIRST PERFORMANCE: Baireuth, Aug. 17, 1876, Hans Richter conducting. London, Her Majesty's Theatre, May 9, 1882, Anton Seidl conducting.

First performance in America, Metropolitan Opera House, Jan. 25, 1888, Anton Seidl conducting, with Lilli Lehmann as *Brünnhilde;* Seidl-Krauss as *Gutrune;* Albert Niemann as *Siegfried;* Adolf Robinson as *Gunther;* Emil Fischer as *Hagen.*

CAST FOR ORIGINAL BAIREUTH PERFORMANCE

Siegfried	tenor		Georg Unger
Gunther, Gibichung ruler	baritone		Eugen Gura
Hagen, his half-brother	bass		F. von Reichenberg
Alberich, Hagen's father	baritone		Carl Hill
Brünnhilde	soprano		Amalia Materna
Gutrune, Gunther's sister	soprano		Mlle. Weckerlin
Waltraute, a valkyrie	contralto		Luise Jaïda

Scenes: The Three Fates on Brünnhilde's rock before dawn; later *Siegfried* and *Brünnhilde*. Hall of the Gibichungs. Hunting party in the forest. Immolation scene and fall of Valhalla.

In recent years at the Metropolitan Opera House, the rôle of *Siegfried* has been sung by Lauritz Melchoir, leading Wagnerian tenor, who also sings the Wagner rôles at Covent Garden, London.

Die Götterdämmerung is the most theatrical of the four operas in the *Ring Cycle,* and requires elaborate scenic effects, especially in the closing scene. The orchestral score contains all of the principal themes heard in the *Cycle* from first to last and it thus becomes a musical resumé of the entire work. It emphasizes the unity of the four operas. Curiously enough the poems or librettos were written by Wagner in reverse order. The last came first which he then called *Siegfried's Death.* He then decided that there must be a "young" Siegfried. This pointed to legendary history leading up to *Siegfried* which became the opera, *The Valkyrie,* and finally Wagner introduced the origin of the legend pertaining to the power of gold through *The Rhinegold* which is a dramatic justification for all that comes later.

GUIDE TO PRONUNCIATION

Gunther	Goon-ter
Gutrune	Goo-troon'-a
Waltraute	Val-trow'-tah
Hagen	Hah'-gen

TRISTAN AND ISOLDE
DIE
LA BOHEM
MADAME BUTTERFLY
FAUST
THE PRIZE SONG
RIGOLET
LOHENGRIN